Of America I

A Beka Book® Pensacola, FL 32523-9100
an affiliate of PENSACOLA CHRISTIAN COLLEGE®

To Parents and Teachers

Children are eagerly searching for a workable sense of values. They need reading material that will give them ideals to reach for and examples to follow.

The stories in this reader have been selected from the readers of America's past and have been edited, modernized, and classroom-tested for student appeal and readability. Many character values are woven throughout the stories. Thought questions at the end of the stories aid in understanding the selections.

Of America I

Fourth Edition

Staff Credits

Compiled by: Beverly Rainey, Phyllis Rand
Edition Editors: Marion Hedquist, Martha Day
Designer: Michelle Johnson
Illustrators: Brian Jekel, Matthew Sample II, Sara Hewitt, Jonathan Taylor, Joe Digangi, and staff

Cataloging Data
      Of America I.—4th ed.
    263 p. : col. ill. ; 23 cm. (A Beka Book reading program)
    1. Readers (Elementary) 2. Reading. I. A Beka Book, Inc.
Library of Congress: PE 1119 .05 2009
Dewey System: 428.6

CONTENTS

*This story could be read during black history month.

Songs and Stories of America *(cont.)*

Makers of America

*This story could be read during black history month.

An American

To be an American is a great honor. One may become a citizen of America by birth or naturalization and yet not be a true American in spirit. To be a real American one must believe in and be loyal to those ideals which have made America what she is.

He must believe in the spirit of freedom as did the pioneers of colonial days, who not only demanded freedom for themselves, but were willing to grant it to others.

He must believe in the common good of the common people and be willing to give up, if necessary, certain things for himself if they injure other people.

He must believe in education as the privilege and duty of all. He must know the history and hero stories of America, and the sacrifices that have been made so that he can enjoy the blessings of freedom.

To be a real American, he must love America above any other country in the world and be willing to vote whenever opportunity offers, to accept public office as a public trust, and to serve the common cause in every way possible. He must honor the American flag as the symbol of his country and protect it from harm or discredit.

To be a real American, he must live in the spirit of America, for the honor of America, and in helpful cooperation with all other Americans.

The Great Were Once As You

Edgar A. Guest

The great were once as you.
They whom men magnify today
Once groped and blundered on life's way.
Were fearful of themselves, and thought
By magic was men's greatness wrought.
They feared to try what they could do;
Yet Fame hath crowned with her success
The selfsame gifts that you possess.

The great were young as you,
Dreaming the very dreams you hold,
Longing, yet fearing, to be bold,
Doubting that they themselves possessed
The strength and skill for every test,
Uncertain of the truths they knew,
Not sure that they could stand to fate
With all the courage of the great.

Then came a day when they
Their first bold venture made,
Scorning to cry for aid.
They dared to stand to fight alone,
Took up the gauntlet life had thrown,
Charged full-front to the fray,
Mastered their fear of self, and then
Learned that our great men are but men.

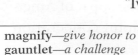

Oh, Youth, go forth and do!
You, too, to fame may rise;
You can be strong and wise.
Stand up to life and play the man—
You can if you'll but think you can;
THE GREAT WERE ONCE AS YOU.
You envy them their proud success?
'Twas won with gifts that you possess.

---

magnify—*give honor to*   fray—*a fight*
gauntlet—*a challenge*

Character

Margaret Slattery

What one is, that is the supreme thing. Sincerity, honesty, unselfishness, intelligence, the spirit of cooperation and justice, cheerfulness, courtesy, concentration and all the rest help make one what he is. What one is—that is Character. Strong, fine character stands the test of life with all its dangers and pitfalls—nothing else does.

Everyone has the power of making his character what it ought to be. The power lies in the little words "Yes" and "No." Saying "Yes" to all that life offers which is good and right, and saying "No" to all that can weaken or defile, will form character strong, pure and fine.

Lincoln and Lee

Author Unknown

Lives of great men all remind us
  We can make our lives sublime,
And, departing, leave behind us
  Footprints on the sands of time.
  —*Henry Wadsworth Longfellow*

Part 1

Young Abe Lincoln

On the twelfth of February, 1809, a boy was born in a cabin in Kentucky. He was named Abraham Lincoln.

His father, Thomas Lincoln, was an idle fellow who could neither read nor write. Sometimes he worked as a farmer, sometimes as a carpenter, but he did little as either.

When Abe was a few years old, Thomas Lincoln made up his mind to go west. He hoped to find rich land and better times.

So he loaded all his worldly goods in a wagon and made his way westward through the forest. In Indiana he stopped and built a house—if house it could be called. It was a room open on one side to the weather. It had no floor, no doors, no windows.

Here they lived a year and then Thomas Lincoln built a cabin. This had a loft in which Abe slept. But there was neither stairway nor ladder by which to mount. Abe climbed up pegs driven in the wall, and slept on the floor on a pile of leaves.

Downstairs there was one bedstead. It was made of poles fastened on one side in a crack of the log wall. On the other side the poles rested on forked sticks driven in the earthen floor. Across the poles were laid boards covered with skins, leaves, and old clothes.

Instead of chairs, in this house there were three-legged stools. There was a rough table, a few dishes, an oven, and a skillet. These were all of the household goods.

When Abe was nine years old, his mother became ill. He and his little sister Sarah nursed her and did the housework. They hoped every day that she would grow better, but instead, she grew worse. No doctor came to see her. There was none within thirty-five miles.

One day Mrs. Lincoln called the children to the bedside. She told them she had not long to live. Laying her

---

bedstead *—the frame of a bed that holds the mattress*

feeble hand on little Abe's head, she told him to be kind to his father and sister.

"Be good to each other, my children," she said. "Love your kin and your God."

A few hours later the children were motherless.

There followed a hard, sad winter. But the next year their father married again—a good, kind woman who took a mother's place. She was gentle and loving; she worked hard and made the best of things. Little Abe and Sarah were treated like her own children. Her love and care made the cabin a home.

Abe was now ten years old and could neither read nor write.

"He must go to school," said his new mother.

So he was sent to a teacher in a log cabin nearby. He studied hard and soon stood at the head of his class. He had few books, but these he read over and over. He did not own an arithmetic book nor a slate. With a piece of charcoal he ciphered on a broad wooden shovel. When it was covered with figures, he shaved them off and used it again.

His father thought it was a waste of time to study so much. He wished Abe to be at work helping him. And so the boy went to school "by littles."

Most of the time he worked barefoot in the field, grubbing, plowing, and mowing. No one his age could carry a heavier load nor strike a harder blow. When he came home he took a piece of cornbread in his hand and sat down to study.

---

kin—*relatives or family members*
ciphered—*worked arithmetic problems*

"by littles"—*a little bit at a time*
grubbing—*digging*

6

So he grew to manhood, tall and strong, awkward and ugly. He was a strange figure with his homespun clothes and his squirrel-skin cap.

Thomas Lincoln now left the Indiana farm, for which he had never paid. Carrying his household goods in an ox wagon, he went west to Illinois.

A little dog trotted near the wagon. One day it fell behind and came up after they had broken the ice and crossed a stream. It was afraid to enter the water covered with floating ice. There it stood, whining and howling on the bank.

"I'll drive back for no dog," said Thomas Lincoln. "Come on! Leave it there."

But kindhearted Abe could not bear to leave the dog in distress. He pulled off his shoes and waded through the icy water. In his arms, he carried the dog across the stream. How it wagged its tail and yelped for joy!

In Illinois a new log cabin was built. Abe helped cut trees, hew timber, and clear away underbrush. He plowed with a team of oxen; he split rails to make a fence.

So passed the days. And now he was twenty-one, a man grown. From the school of the backwoods, he started out in the world for himself.

A Virginia Boy

Let me tell you about a Virginia home, very different from the Lincoln cabin in Kentucky. This was a handsome old country house called Stratford. It was built in the shape of the letter H. On the roof were summer houses where bands played on summer evenings. Around it were broad grounds, sloping down to a beautiful river.

It was a grand old house, and when my story begins it was a happy home. Here lived General Henry Lee, called "Light Horse Harry."

His forefathers had held place and rank in England. They had come to Virginia in its early days, and in war and in peace they had been leaders.

"Light Horse Harry" had been a brave officer in the War for Independence. He married a beautiful, gentle lady, and the home at Stratford was made glad by children. There were four sons and two daughters.

The youngest son was Robert Edward Lee, born January 19, 1807.

When Robert was four years old, his father moved from Stratford. He was sorry to leave his home, but he wished his children to be near good schools. As soon as they were old enough, his sons were sent to the best teachers.

All did well at school, Robert best of all. He studied hard and was faithful to every task. If he had to draw on his slate a figure to be rubbed out the next minute, he did it with care.

"Whatever is worth doing at all," he thought, "is worth doing well."

His teachers praised him; his comrades loved him. In the schoolroom and on the playground he was the leader.

The first cloud on his happy childhood was the illness of his father. General Lee left home, hoping to gain health and strength. His older sons, too, were away from home, one at college, one in the navy. One of his daughters was in ill health and the other was a child.

Thus to Robert came the care of his sick mother. He nursed her, he kept house, he obeyed her every wish.

In the afternoons his friends called in vain, "Come, Robert! Let us play ball. Robert, Robert! Come and go skating."

He shook his head and answered, "I must hurry home to take mother driving. She is lonely and not well. Now that my father and brothers are away, I am the man of the house."

"How could I do without him?" said his mother. "He is both son and daughter to me."

"Robert was always good," wrote his father. He asked if his sons rode and shot well. He wished them to ride and shoot well and always to speak the truth.

These three Robert did. Gentle and good as he was, he was no milksop. He was brave and active, first in manly sports.

The hope that the father would grow strong was all in vain. He grew worse and died far away from home. More than ever, Robert became his mother's mainstay, her right hand.

It was a sad parting when he left home. But it came time to prepare for his life work, and he wished to be a soldier like his father.

So he went to West Point, a school for soldiers. There he remained four years. In all that time he never got a mark or a reproof for bad conduct. His gun was always bright, his clothes were always neat, his lessons were always learned. He did not think that mischief was "fun." He obeyed the rules and studied hard. He stood next to head in a class of nearly fifty.

At last his schooldays were over. The handsome young cadet went home with honors to his mother.

---

milksop—*a boy or man who lacks courage or manliness*

mainstay—*the main support*
cadet—*a military school student*

That loving mother was not to be with him long. For years she had not been strong, and now day by day she grew more feeble. Day and night Robert sat at her bedside. His hand gave all her food and medicine and smoothed her pillow. She died blessing God for the love and care of such a son.

Now Robert Lee stood at the threshold of life. Behind him lay a long line of honored forefathers. He had gentle home training and the best schooling.

Honest Abe

As a boy Abraham Lincoln plowed and grubbed, planted corn, and split rails for his father. At twenty-one he began life on his own account.

For a long time he kept on with the same homely labors. He plowed and grubbed for the neighboring farmers. He bought his homespun clothes by splitting rails.

He loved to hear and tell jokes, but he did not idle away his leisure time. He read all the books he could get and made speeches to rocks and trees.

One spring he went down to New Orleans with a boatload of meat, corn, and hogs. For the first time he saw slaves bought and sold.

The blacks in this country were not free then. They were slaves. They had been brought to America by the Dutch and sold as slaves in both the northern and the southern states. The North was too cold for them to live and work there, however, so they were sold and sent to the cotton and tobacco fields of the South.

In Lincoln's day there were few slaves in the North. Neither he nor his friends owned any. It did not seem

---

homely labors—*work that is typical of home life*

right to him that men and women should be bought and sold like cattle.

He said, "If ever I get a chance to hit that thing, I'll hit it hard."

From New Orleans he went back home. For a while he kept a country store. In his spare time he studied hard to make up for his lack of schooling. One day he walked six miles to borrow a grammar book. When he had five minutes to spare, he gave it to his book which he kept always at hand.

But he did not neglect his work. If he made a mistake, he did not rest until it was set right. One day a woman came in and bought some goods. He made an error of a few cents in her change. That night when he shut the store he went to return her money before he slept.

He was honest in word and deed. People liked him and called him "Honest Abe."

After a time Lincoln and a friend opened a store of their own. But Lincoln spent his time reading and studying law, and the partner spent his time drinking. No wonder they failed.

His partner died soon after and Lincoln took on himself all their debts. No one could have made him pay them, but he thought it was right to do so. The debt of a few hundred dollars was a great deal to this poor man. It took him fifteen years to pay it, but pay it he did, down to the last cent.

By cutting wood, splitting rails, and other work, Lincoln managed to get bread and meat. He kept on with his study of law.

One noon a man for whom he worked found him sitting barefoot on a woodpile, a book in his hand.

"What are you reading?" asked the man.

"I'm not reading," was the answer, "I'm studying."

"Studying what?"

"Law, sir," was the reply.

The man laughed, but Lincoln kept on studying.

He worked for a while with a surveyor and learned to measure land. He was postmaster as well as surveyor. The mail came only once a week. He carried the letters in his hat and gave them out as he went about to measure land. What do you think of having a hat for a post office?

The man Lincoln had not outgrown the kindheartedness of his boyhood.

One day as he was going along dressed in his best clothes, he saw a pig squirming and squealing with distress stuck in a mudhole.

Lincoln did not wish to soil his clothes getting it out, so he passed on. But it seemed to him that the poor thing grunted, "Ugh! There, now! My last hope is gone!" So he turned back and helped it out of the mud.

Mr. Lincoln worked hard at the study of law. He thought much and talked well about public questions, too. He made people laugh at his funny stories and clever sayings. Men thought so highly of him that they sent him to help make laws for the state.

After he came home, he moved to Springfield and began to practice law. He carried with him in a saddle bag his worldly goods—a few garments and two or three law books.

Would you like to know how he looked? He was very tall, lean, and awkward. He had a sallow, wrinkled face; coarse dark hair; a large, crooked nose; and beautiful eyes. His clothes were coarse and ill-fitting. In one hand he carried a carpetbag containing papers. In the other was a faded green cotton umbrella with a piece of cord tied round the middle.

But as people listened to his words, full of wit, wisdom, and common sense, no one thought of how he looked or dressed—only of what he said.

In Springfield he married Miss Mary Todd, a pretty and clever young lady. But people who knew her shook their heads and said, "Her temper is not good. She will not make a happy home."

Her husband drifted more and more into public life. Whenever a great question came up, people wished to know what he thought about it. When he was younger, they had sent him to help make laws for the state. Now they sent him to Washington to help make the nation's laws.

This pleased his wife very much. She began to be proud of her husband, ugly and awkward, but clever and wise.

The time was at hand when he was to become a leader among men. In 1856, he aided in forming a new political party, called the Republican Party. Its main object was to prevent the spread of slavery.

Lincoln said that the United States could not remain as it was, half free and half slave. He wished all to be free.

In May 1860, the Republicans held a meeting to decide whom they wished for President.

"Let it be 'Honest old Abe, the railsplitter,'" they said.

So Lincoln was elected President of the United States.

Before he started to Washington, he slipped away from the crowds who came to ask places and favors. He went to see his father's grave and to visit his stepmother, his second mother. With tears streaming down her cheeks, the good old woman gave him her blessing.

The friends of his boyhood clasped his hand. They were proud of "Honest Abe," who had risen from a barefoot boy to President of our great country.

Then Lincoln went to Washington. With him went his wife and three sons, Robert, William, and Thomas. Thomas, or "Tad," as the baby was called, was just seven.

Mr. Lincoln was a kind and loving father. He was never too busy to let the boys play in his office. They dragged books from the shelves, pulled out papers, and upset the ink. Other people frowned, but their father only laughed. They were a wellspring of joy, his one comfort in the sad, hard days that were at hand.

---

wellspring—*the source*

The Young Captain

While Abraham Lincoln was making his way in the West, in the South Robert Lee rose in his chosen calling.

When he left West Point, he was made engineer. This is the work which is given the men who stand highest in their class. Engineers, a great soldier says, are as needful to an army as sails to a ship. In peace they plan forts and direct the course of rivers and do other useful work. In war they build roads and bridges, they study the ground to be traveled over, they guide the movements of armies.

Two years after he left West Point, he married a young lady he had known and loved from boyhood. This was the gentle and beautiful Miss Mary Custis, the only child of Washington's adopted son. Her beautiful old home, Arlington, is just across the river from Washington, D.C. Here Lee and his wife made their home.

Their slaves were well-fed and well-clothed. But neither Lieutenant Lee nor his father-in-law believed in owning slaves, so both set their slaves free.

Lieutenant Lee had a happy home those first years of his married life. He had many friends, and he was never known to speak ill of anyone.

Dear as were home and friends, duty came first with him. And now his duty as a soldier called him far from home. He was ordered to the West to make stronger and higher the banks of the Mississippi River.

Out West he kept busy with his work and with his studies. He learned a great deal about war from books. Soon he was to learn still more from life.

Our country quarreled with Mexico and the two
countries went to war. Captain Lee was sent with other
soldiers to Mexico. About the time he went there to
fight, Mr. Lincoln went as a lawmaker to Washington.

Many stories could be told of Lee's brave deeds in
Mexico.

Once he was sent to find out where the enemy was.
Mile after mile he rode in their country. At last he came
to what seemed an army.

"See, there are the tents white in the moonlight,"
said his guide. "Let us go back."

But Captain Lee said, "No," he would ride on to get
fuller news. Lo! what seemed to be tents was a flock
of sheep. The drovers said that the army had not yet
crossed the mountains. So back twenty miles galloped

Captain Lee with the news. He rested only three hours and then marched off at the head of some soldiers.

Before one battle, seven officers were sent across rough, rocky country with orders to men on the other side. Six came back saying they could not cross. Only one went on. That one was Robert Lee.

He set to work with some men making a road across which to guide the soldiers. Alone, in darkness, in driving rain, he rode back to tell the general what he had done and what he planned to do. The general said that this midnight journey was the greatest deed of the war.

There were many brave soldiers in this war. Of them all none was more loved in the camp nor more admired on the battlefield than Captain Robert Lee.

In camp and on the battlefield his thoughts were often with his wife and children at home. He wrote them long, loving letters. He told them how the bullets whistled round him in the fight. He wondered where he would put his little son, if he were there, to keep him safe.

He told them about his horses, which he loved. He had to ride them very hard, sometimes fifty or sixty miles a day. While his family was eating their Christmas dinner, he lay on the ground beside his horse, watching for the enemy.

At last the war was over. Captain Lee went home with honor. How glad his wife and children were to see him!

But he did not stay in Virginia long. He was sent to take charge of the soldiers' school at West Point. Here he had the pleasure of seeing his son, Custis, stand at the head of his class.

Now Captain Lee was made colonel. He was sent to Texas to fight against the Indians. Far as he was from home, he kept close to his wife and children by loving letters. He kept close to God, too, and led a pure, noble life.

He wrote home how he spent the Fourth of July in Texas. He had just had a march of thirty miles. He made a sunshade of his blanket, raised on four sticks driven into the ground. The sun was fiery hot, the air was like a blast from a furnace, the water was salty.

But he said his love for his country and his faith in her were as strong as they could have been under better circumstances.

In his letters to his youngest daughter, he asked about Tom Tita, a large yellow cat, the pet of Arlington. He told about a Texas cat which he saw dressed for company. It was snow white, with tail and feet tipped with black. Around its neck was a chain of gold. It had holes bored in each ear and in these holes were bows of pink and blue ribbon. "Its round face set in pink and blue looked like a big owl in a full blooming ivy bush," said he.

In February, 1861, Colonel Lee was called home from Texas. Great events were at hand. For the last time he was with his family at beloved Arlington.

Character Theme—Perseverance &
Honor/Duty

Time to Think

1. Who encouraged Abraham Lincoln to go to school?
2. What are some of the differences between the childhoods of Lincoln and Lee?
3. How did Lincoln feel about the issue of slavery?
4. What was the first war that Lee fought in?
5. Where did Robert E. Lee live with his wife and children?
6. In what ways were Lincoln and Lee alike?

Lincoln and Lee

Part 2

President and General

Now came the spring of 1861. With it came war, war between the states.

The states of the North and the South had been quarreling for many years. They differed as to the taxes they should pay and the way the country should be ruled. They differed as to whether people should have slaves or not. Hot-headed people on both sides said bitter things. The more they quarreled, the angrier they became.

The Southern people were sorry to see Lincoln made President. They did not know much about him, but they knew that he was leader of a party which wished to put an end to slavery.

Some of them said, "We are only partners in this Union. Since we cannot stay together in peace, let us part. We will have a government of our own here in the South."

But Lincoln and the North behind him said, "No, the United States all make up one great country. No one can draw out when it pleases."

Lincoln said the Southern states should be made to stay in the Union. So he called for seventy-five thousand soldiers to send against them. He needed a good general to put at the head of this army. Who should it be? General Scott, who had led the army in Mexico, was too old.

Scott said, "Robert Lee is the best soldier I ever saw in the field. He will show himself the foremost captain of his time. Make him chief of the army. He will be worth fifty thousand men to you."

So President Lincoln sent and asked Lee to take charge of his army.

Lee said no. He loved the army and he loved the Union. "If the four million slaves in the South were mine," he said, "I would give them all up to keep the Union." Virginia was his mother state, though, and he could not fight against her.

"I must go with Virginia," he said.

He gave up his place in the United States Army and took command of the Virginia troops.

For four years there was war in our land. Friend fought against friend, brother against brother. There was much hate and bitterness. But high above this, as mountains above clouds, rose two men, the greatest of all.

Lincoln said, "We are not enemies, but friends. We must be friends." He looked at both sides of the question. He said that the Southern people were just what the Northern ones would be in their places. If people in the North owned slaves, they would not wish to give them up.

He hoped some plan would be agreed on to free the slaves in time by paying for them. Now he said the fight was not to free the slaves but to keep the Union. He loved his country and wanted it to be one great country forever.

Lee, too, never used the word "enemies" in talking about the people of the North. He spoke of them as "those people." "I never saw the day when I did not pray for them," he said.

I have told you how Lincoln looked. Would you like to have a picture of Lee? He was called the handsomest man in the army. He was tall, straight, broad-shouldered. His eyes were dark and his hair was beginning to grow white. He was neat in dress and person and sat gracefully on his handsome horse.

During the first of the war, Lee was sent to fight in western Virginia. Then he went south to strengthen the coast against attack. There were few troops and poor guns, but he put them where they would do the most good.

Then he came back to Virginia. For a little while he was with his wife and children. But they were not now, nor ever again, at beautiful Arlington. It was in the hands of the Northern soldiers. General Lee tried to comfort his wife for their loss. He told her that wherever they went they could carry in their hearts the memory of their beautiful, happy old home.

Lee took charge of the army near Richmond.

Up in the Valley of Virginia were some brave soldiers under a great general. This was Stonewall Jackson. He thought that fighting and praying were the whole duty of man. His enemies never knew when and where he was going to strike and strike hard. Later in the war they said they could tell by a simple rule where he would be. Where he was least wanted and least expected, he was sure to turn up.

After the first battle, the North saw that the war would not be over in a few days or weeks. Lincoln called for soldiers for three years, instead of for three months as at first. The army was put in order and well supplied. Then it marched against Richmond.

The great trouble which Lincoln had from the first was in the choice of generals. He had brave soldiers, as many as were needed. But who was the general able and wise enough to lead them? Some said this man, some said that.

Lincoln tried one general. Battles were lost and time was wasted. Then he tried another and another. His one wish was to put the right man in the right place. Do you think the war would have lasted so long if Lee had taken charge of the United States Army in 1861?

But there were good officers in the North as well as in the South. You shall hear how in the end Lincoln found and supported a great general.

Meanwhile, as I told you, the army of the North was in sight of Richmond. Some of the Southern officers thought Lee ought to retreat. But he led the soldiers forward to the masterly Seven Days' fight near Rich-

mond. The Northern army fell back, fighting as it went.
It was full of brave soldiers. Here was American against
American.

Lee marched north at the head of his army. But he
lost ten thousand men and fought a battle in which neither side could claim the victory.

General Lee was staying in a tent because he did not
wish anyone to give up a house for him. Three stars on
his coat collar were the only signs of his rank. His food
was plain, and his table was set with tinware. When
dainty dishes were sent him, he gave them to wounded
soldiers or sick prisoners.

He had no small vices, such as smoking, drinking,
and chewing. No one ever accused him of great ones. In
small things and great, he was loving and unselfish. He
would take the least comfortable chair for himself. He
would take, too, the blame for mistakes made by other
generals and allow them the credit which belonged to him.

The war had been started to keep the Union. But
many people of the North wished to put an end to slavery.
President Lincoln felt that it would help the cause of the
Union to free the slaves. So he declared them free.

About this time Lincoln tried another general. He
was called "Fighting Joe," but General Lee soon made
him run. Yet the victory was worse than a defeat for the
South. Stonewall Jackson was killed, mistakenly shot by
his own men.

"I have lost my right arm," said General Lee.

The South now lacked men and money, food and
clothing. The soldiers were overworked and underfed.
They marched, they fought, they marched and fought

---

vices—*evil practices or habits*

again. But they laughed and their guns were clean and their swords were bright. General Lee said there was one time when he was never ashamed of the looks of his soldiers. That was when they were fighting.

Again Lee marched North. He met the Union army at Gettysburg. This time there was against them an able general, as well as brave soldiers. And neither the time nor the place was what General Lee would have chosen.

He made his plans well and gave his orders: "Get the troops ready. Form line of battle. Attack."

But one officer failed in his duty. He did not go forward when he was told. The men whom he ought to have helped fell and died before the Northern guns. The soldiers who died did not fail "Master Robert." How he missed his "right arm" Jackson!

Lee did not speak one word of useless blame to the man whose fault lost the battle. Back he marched with his brave men to Virginia. On the way sad news met him. He learned that his son "Rooney" was a prisoner.

A few months later President Lincoln went to Gettysburg. He did not go to fight. He went to set the place apart as a burial ground for soldiers. He made a brief, beautiful speech. He said that the brave soldiers who died there had hallowed the ground. They had done their part and that well. It was for the living to do theirs—to keep "government of the people, by the people, for the people."

The war had now been going on about three years, and President Lincoln at last found a general such as he wished. This was Grant the hammer. You shall hear how he hammered at the army of Lee till he pounded it to pieces. He fought at first, and that well, in the West. Some people found fault with him, but the President said, "I can't spare this man: he fights."

So he told Grant to come east and take charge of the army.

With many brave boys in blue, well fed and well supplied, Grant started out. He made up his mind to take Richmond, if fighting and time could do it.

Against Grant, Lee led his soldiers in ragged gray. Day after day came battles. Men of the same blood fought like wild beasts in the woods. But whenever a man fell in Grant's army, another filled the gap. A man killed in Lee's army left an empty place. The South had sent even her boys and old men to fight. She had no more to give and no money to hire troops.

In 1864 the President of the United States had to be chosen. Some people wanted Lincoln again. Some did not. About this time he saw that the army needed more men.

"Do not call for them now," said his friends. "It will make trouble and people will think all is not going well. They will not vote for you. Wait a few weeks until you are made President."

"What is the Presidency worth to me if I have no country?" asked Lincoln. And he sent out the call for five hundred thousand soldiers. He loved his country more than place and power for himself.

But the people were learning to love and trust him. A second time he was chosen President. They had the right man in the right place and they wished to keep him there.

In 1860 the President's speech showed his great desire to keep off war. But war came.

Now in 1864 the end of the war was in sight. His speech this time showed his great desire to keep off bitterness and hate. He wished himself and all men to go on "with malice toward none, with charity for all, with firmness in the right as God gives us to see the right."

About the time that Lincoln was made President of the United States, Lee was given command of the army of the Confederacy.

An Irishman who came to the army was asked what he thought of the Southern soldiers.

"Oh, I never saw men fight better," he answered, "but they don't eat enough."

Poor fellows! They had little to eat, little to wear. Flour was two hundred fifty dollars a barrel, coffee twelve dollars a pound, and tea thirty-five dollars.

One day General Lee went tired and sad to Richmond. "A cup of tea would do him good," thought a lady. She had enough tea to make one cup, only one. The polite, unselfish gentleman would not drink it if he knew this. So she filled her cup with muddy water and his with tea. As he drank the tea, she sipped the water.

Day after day, week after week, Lee worked to make small means equal great. It cost Grant thirty days and sixty thousand men to march seventy-five miles. But the time came when Lee could hold out no longer. The boys in gray fell back and the boys in blue marched into Richmond. President Lincoln and General Grant walked up and down the streets of the smoking, ruined city.

General Lee hoped to get away with his little army and marched away to the southwest. But by mistake food was carried past them and the soldiers were left without a crust. They could not fight; they could not march.

"I would rather die a thousand deaths than surrender," said General Lee. Yet he saw that it must be done, and delay would cause useless waste of brave lives. So he surrendered to General Grant.

Grant, too, was a hero, brave and noblehearted. He had asked the President what he must do with the men who gave up.

"If I were in your place," said Lincoln, "I'd let 'em up easy, I'd let 'em up easy."

And so General Grant did. He left the soldiers their horses to work their farms. When he learned that they had only parched corn to eat, he hastened to send them food.

When General Lee spoke for the last time to his soldiers, they sobbed aloud. Tears were in his eyes, too.

"Men, we have fought the war together," he said. "I have done my best for you. My heart is too full to say more."

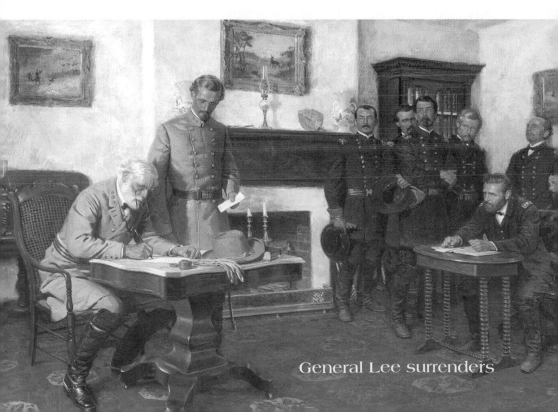

General Lee surrenders

Then he mounted Traveller, his good gray horse, and rode away.

General Grant sent President Lincoln word that General Lee had surrendered. The war was over.

Lincoln was full of joy. How he had longed for peace and goodwill, a reunited country! He said the Southern states had no right to leave the Union and so they were still in it and had their rights as states. Gentle and great-hearted as he was, he wished to forgive and forget the past.

Had President Lincoln lived, much might have been well done that was ill done. But alas! his death was near.

On the evening of April 14, 1865, he went with his wife to the theater. An actor named Booth crept up to him, drew a pistol, and fired. The President fell, sorely wounded. Friends crowded around him; doctors were called. Too late! The wicked work was done. Lincoln was dying. It was a sad funeral train which moved west, past city after city, through state after state. A nation left work and play to mourn its dead chief.

Great as was the loss to the North, it was even greater to the South. A harder task than war was before the country. Lincoln's great heart full of justice and mercy, his iron will and common sense would have been equal to this task. But he was dead and there was no second Lincoln. It was left to clumsy hands and bitter hearts to settle matters between the North and the South.

General Lee urged his people to be patient and to make the best of things. To a lady who spoke angrily against the North, he said gently, "Madam, do not train up your children as foes to the United States. We are one country now. Bring them up to be Americans."

General Lee was poor and homeless, but he would take no aid. At a small salary he became president of Washington College in Virginia. He helped boys to become better and wiser men. As the soldiers loved him, so did the students; a word from him would rule the wildest.

His home life was happy, troubled only by his failing health. One evening as he stood at the tea table to ask a blessing, his voice failed and he sank in a chair. He lingered a few days, wandering in thought to battlefields, and then died, October 12, 1870.

Behind his coffin was led his riderless horse. Bells tolled. Men, women, and children wept as if a member of their own home were dead. A great general, a great, good man, had passed away.

You have here the story of two of the world's great men.

One rose from a log cabin to the President's chair. He ruled the country wisely in a troubled time and died with the laurels of peace and victory.

The other was the flower of a noble race. But the cause for which he fought was lost, and his was the thorny crown of defeat.

Both were heroes. Each did right as he saw right and filled a great place wisely and nobly. Of each, Americans have cause to be proud.

---

laurels—*wreaths of leaves given as a sign of victory*

Character Theme—Loyalty/Duty
& Selflessness

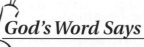

God's Word Says   *Ephesians 4:31–32*

Let all bitterness, and wrath, and anger,
and clamor, and evil speaking, be put away
from you, with all malice: And be ye kind
one to another, tenderhearted, forgiving one
another, even as God for Christ's sake hath
forgiven you.

Time to Think

1. What happened in the spring of 1861?
2. Why did Lee say no when Lincoln asked him to lead the Union army?
3. Who did President Lincoln finally find to lead the Union army successfully after three years of war?
4. What was the condition of the Southern army when Lee was made general?
5. Why did Lee finally surrender?
6. Explain why Lincoln and Lee were both heroes for their cause and for America.

> No race can prosper till it learns there is as
> much dignity in tilling a field as in writing a poem.
> —*Booker T. Washington*

Booker T. Washington

Educator
Basil Miller

Booker T. Washington dedicated his life to helping his
fellow black Americans. He taught them to gain acceptance
in society by developing high standards and by striving
to do their best. For over thirty years, he was recognized
as the most influential spokesman for his race.
By his life, he set an example for all Americans to follow.

The face of the black woman was radiant as she knelt
in prayer. From his rag pallet on the floor, a boy watched
his mother. She prayed, "Here I am an' my children, just
slaves. Look on us with pity an' give us freedom, dear
God, please to give us freedom."

The lad closed his eyes as his mother rose from her knees and looked toward the corner where her children were sleeping.

pallet—*a narrow, poor bed*

33

"Slaves"—the word lodged in his mind. *He was a slave.*

Young Booker had been born sometime before the outbreak of the Civil War, but he did not know the date, for slaves' children were numerous, and who wanted to bother to record the birth of another? Booker's mother, Jane, was the cook on a plantation near Hale Ford, Virginia, but the boy had never seen his father.

When Booker was a small child, the Civil War was raging. Mother Jane's prayer was to be answered. She and her children were to be free! The hope of freedom gave her the courage to face each day. How fervently she prayed that her boys and her daughter might grow up to be free!

There was great excitement one spring day at the plantation. The slaves huddled together in small groups, talking excitedly. When the announcement came for all of them to assemble at the master's house, Mammy Jane knew that the long-awaited day had come. The war was over. She and her children were free.

Meanwhile, Booker's stepfather (his mother had married a slave from a near-by farm) had gone to West Virginia. Soon he sent for his wife and daughter, and the two boys. It was a long, hard journey. Putting their few belongings in an old cart, they walked, pushing the cart, for many weeks through strange country, until at last they reached Malden, West Virginia.

Freedom meant the privilege to work for a living. The stepfather hired out the two young boys to work in the salt mines. Booker had dreamed of going to school, but though now he was free, he was no closer to his dream than before.

"Never you mind, honey," his Mammy Jane consoled him, "you'll learn some day."

Life for the little boy, not yet ten, was hard. He rose at four each morning and worked long hours. Noticing that there were strange markings on the various barrels of salt Booker asked what the mysterious symbols meant. He found they were numbers, and soon he could recognize the number 18, which was on all the barrels he handled. Mammy Jane was able to get him a copy of Webster's speller. He studied this for hours, as he learned his alphabet and spelled the strange words.

Booker longed desperately to attend school. When his stepfather refused permission, Booker asked if he could attend the evening school, provided he continued his day work. The teacher was willing to help this intelligent young boy, and the stepfather agreed.

While Booker was playing marbles one Sunday, an old gentleman invited him to Sunday school. Booker accepted the invitation and became a faithful member. Realizing that his wife's son was an unusual child, the stepfather finally permitted Booker to attend day school, provided he worked in the salt mines from four to nine in the morning and after school until dark.

When he went to school the first day, the teacher began by calling the roll. Booker noticed that each child had not only one but two names. The only name he had was Booker, but by the time the teacher reached him, he had decided on the second.

---

consoled—*comforted*

"Booker Washington, sir," he answered the teacher. The black boy had named himself.

He was unable to remain long in school, for the family was poor, and the money he would make in the mines was sorely needed. This was a harsh blow. Hearing of a school at Hampton where needy black boys could receive an education, Booker Washington decided to leave home and go there. After a walk of many days, the dirty boy presented himself to the head of the school. Something in the lad's eyes would not allow the superintendent to turn him away.

The boy had made the long journey of more than five hundred miles on foot. He had slept under porches and worked to earn his food. He was given the task of sweeping and dusting a room. The room was thoroughly swept, not once but three times, and when the superintendent returned, not a particle of dust remained. Consequently, Booker Washington was permitted to earn his education by working as janitor.

The president of the institution found a sponsor to pay the brilliant lad's yearly tuition of seventy dollars. Booker continued to work for room and board.

The young student wished that his mother could have lived to see him graduate with honors, after which he returned to become the village school-

superintendent—*director or supervisor*

teacher at Malden. Here he devoted himself to educating the black people, both old and young. Night and day he taught all who had the will to learn.

Feeling the need of further education, Washington enrolled in the Wayland Seminary, where he studied for eight months. At the age of twenty-one he was becoming known as an orator and willingly granted a request to stump the country. This involved making speeches in favor of changing the capital of West Virginia from Wheeling to Charleston.

His success was so great that many urged him to make politics his life work, but Booker Washington had a different ambition. How eagerly the people of Malden had responded to education! Here was the way to help his race. He would train intelligent blacks as teachers and leaders of his countrymen. But how could this vision be accomplished?

When a commencement orator was needed for graduation exercises at Hampton, his old school, the honor student was invited to speak. His address, "The Face that Wins," made such a favorable impression that Washington was asked to join the faculty.

His first class was a group of Indians who had been taken from their reservations to Hampton to be trained at government expense. His evenings were devoted to teaching a large class of poor black Americans who could not afford to attend day school.

The opportunity for which he had so long searched finally presented itself. When the legislature of Alabama

---

stump—*travel around making speeches*
commencement orator—*the speaker at a graduation ceremony*

legislature—*the group of people that makes the laws*

decided to have a normal school for black people in their state, they appropriated funds and asked the president of Hampton to select a suitable person as school superintendent.

Washington was elated when told, "I believe you are the right person to take charge of the new school in Alabama. Would you be willing to accept the position?"

"I believe I can fill it, and am willing to try," he said. Here was his opportunity—a school where black people could be trained to teach, funds to be supplied by Alabama. After a brief visit home, Washington left for the place he was to make famous, Tuskegee, Alabama.

A discouraging situation met him. Although two thousand dollars a year had been appropriated for salaries, there had been no provision for lands or buildings. Where could these be found? Washington began his search. To everyone he met he said, "I'm going to start a school," and described the situation. Soon he had many friends who trusted this energetic young man of their own race.

Conditions were wretched: Blacks were living in shanties little better than pigsties. The only churches were outdoor meetings; there were no schools.

"These, my people, are free, but they do not know how to use their freedom. They must be educated and learn to wish for the worthwhile. I will do all I can for them," Washington declared.

On Independence Day, 1881, Washington's school opened in a tumble-down chicken coop. In six weeks there were fifty pupils. Meanwhile, Hampton sent a helper, Olivia Davidson who assisted Washington greatly.

normal school—*a school that trains teachers*
appropriated—*set apart for something specific*

elated—*full of joy*
shanties—*small cabins or shacks*

Just outside Tuskegee was a dilapidated plantation of no use to anyone, which was for sale for five hundred dollars. Washington, after inspecting it, knew he wanted it. With the help of Hampton's president, he purchased the property.

"If you have axes, bring them to school tomorrow," he told his pupils. "If you haven't any, I'll supply you. School will be dismissed early, and then we'll have a chopping bee." Washington determined that he and the pupils would erect new buildings and repair the old ones.

Meanwhile, the money owing on the plantation was soon to fall due. Booker Washington and Olivia began to solicit contributions to complete payments on the school. The gift that touched Booker's heart most deeply came from an old woman.

She said, "I don't have any money, but I want you to take these six eggs, and I want you to put these eggs into the education of those boys and girls."

A great sorrow entered Washington's life at this time. He had married Fannie Smith, whom he had known at Malden. Shortly after bearing him a daughter, Portia, his wife died.

Meanwhile, Porter Hall had been built, chiefly by the students and Washington. The bricks were baked in a homemade kiln. When the first three kilns failed to burn the bricks properly, Washington pawned his watch and used the money to build another kiln. This proved successful, and the lovely structure soon began to rise.

Needing more funds than could possibly be raised in the South, Washington began to tour the Northern states.

---

dilapidated—*rundown*
erect—*build*
solicit—*to try to gain by persuasion*

kiln—*an oven used to bake clay or ceramics*
pawned—*received money in exchange for a possession*

Earnestly he described the needs, and on his first lecture tour ten thousand dollars was raised.

Already Booker T. Washington had begun to fill the place of black leadership. In 1896 Harvard presented him with an honorary Master of Arts Degree, the first ever awarded to a black American. President Eliot, in presenting it, addressed Booker thus: "Teacher; wise helper of his race; good servant of God and country."

"If through me, a humble representative," Washington replied, "seven million of my people in the South might be permitted to send a message to Harvard, that message would be: Tell them that the sacrifice was not in vain. Tell them that by way of the shop, the field, the skilled hand, habits of thrift and economy, by way of industrial school and college, we are coming. We are crawling up, working

---

honorary—*given to show honor*

up, yea, bursting up. There is no power on earth that can permanently stay our progress!"

Washington made three trips to Europe, and each time he returned with new determination, not only to fight for his own race, but for all the downtrodden of every race.

By 1915 the strain proved too great. While on a trip to New York, his health broke completely, and Washington knew his end was near. He asked to be taken back to the place he loved and founded: Tuskegee Institute. The following day Booker T. Washington was dead. His passing created sorrow in the hearts of many, but he lives on in the lives of the young people whom he trained and influenced.

---

downtrodden—*those who are mistreated*

Character Theme—Diligence & Service/Compassion

Time to Think

1. When was Booker T. Washington born?
2. What was Booker's "entrance test" into Hampton?
3. What school did Booker T. Washington start?
4. How did he raise the funds to build the school?
5. What made Booker T. Washington a great man?

Freedom

James Russell Lowell

They are slaves who fear to speak
For the fallen and the weak;
They are slaves who will not choose
Hatred, scoffing and abuse,
Rather than in silence shrink
From the truth they needs must think.
They are slaves who dare not be
In the right with two or three.

Secrets of Success

Whosoever will be great among you,
let him be your minister; and whosoever
will be chief among you, let him be your
servant: even as the Son of man came
not to be ministered unto, but to minister,
and to give His life a ransom for many.

—*Matthew 20:26–28*

Be strong and of a good courage:
for unto this people shalt thou divide
for an inheritance the land, which I
sware unto their fathers to give them.

Only be thou strong and very
courageous, that thou mayest observe to
do according to all the law, which Moses
my servant commanded thee: turn not
from it to the right hand or to the left,
that thou mayest prosper whithersoever
thou goest.

This book of the law shall not depart
out of thy mouth; but thou shalt meditate
therein day and night, that thou mayest
observe to do according to all that is
written therein: for then thou shalt make
thy way prosperous, and then thou shalt
have good success.

Have not I commanded thee?
Be strong and of a good courage; be not
afraid, neither be thou dismayed: for the
Lord thy God is with thee whithersoever
thou goest. —*Joshua 1:6–9*

---

ransom—*a price paid to release a hostage*

43

The Wright Brothers

Quentin Reynolds

Quentin Reynolds, the famous war correspondent and writer, tells how Wilbur and Orville Wright learned their first principles in the science of flight at their home in Dayton, Ohio, in 1878— and how they later put them to work at Kitty Hawk in 1903.

Learning from Mother

Susan Wright wasn't like other mothers. She was younger and prettier than most other mothers, and she liked to laugh and she liked to play games with her three youngest children: Wilbur, who was eleven; Orville, who was seven; and Katharine, who was four.

The other mothers would shake their heads and say, "Susan Wright spoils those children; lets 'em do anything they want. No good will come of it."

But Susan Wright only laughed. In the summer she'd pack a picnic lunch and she, the two boys and little Kate (no one ever called her Katharine) would go and spend a day in the woods. Mrs. Wright knew the name of every bird and she could tell a bird by his song. Wilbur and Orville learned to tell birds too.

One day they sat on the banks of a river near Dayton, where they lived. Wilbur and Orville were fishing. Everyone called Wilbur "Will," and of course Orville was "Orv." The fish weren't biting very well. Suddenly a big bird swooped down, stuck his long bill into the river, came out with a tiny fish, and then swooped right up into the sky again.

"What makes a bird fly, Mother?" Wilbur asked.

"Their wings, Will," she said. "You notice they move their wings and that makes them go faster."

"But Mother," Will said, not quite satisfied, "that bird that just swooped down didn't even move his wings. He swooped down, grabbed a fish, and then went right up again. He never moved his wings at all."

"The wind doesn't just blow *toward* you or *away* from you," she said. "It blows *up* and *down,* too. When a current of air blows up, it takes the bird up. His wings support him in the air."

"If we had wings, then we could fly too, couldn't we, Mother?" Wilbur asked.

"But God didn't give us wings." She laughed.

"Maybe we could make wings," Wilbur insisted.

"Maybe," his mother said thoughtfully. "But I don't know. No one ever did make wings that would allow a boy to fly."

"I will some day," Wilbur said, and Orville nodded and said, "I will, too."

"Well, when you're a little older maybe you can try," their mother said.

That was another thing about Susan Wright. Most other mothers would have thought this to be foolish talk. Most other mothers would have said, "Oh, don't be silly, who ever heard of such nonsense!" But not Susan Wright. She knew that even an eleven-year-old boy can have ideas of his own, and just because they happened to come from an eleven-year-old head—well, that didn't make them foolish. She never treated her children as if they were babies, and perhaps that's why they liked to go fishing with her or on picnics with her. And that's why they kept asking her questions. She always gave them sensible answers.

They asked their father questions too, but he was a traveling minister and he was away a lot.

"It's getting chilly," Mrs. Wright said suddenly. "Look at those gray clouds, Will."

Wilbur looked up. "It's going to snow, I bet," he said happily.

"No more picnics until next spring," his mother said. "Yes, it looks like snow. We'd better be getting home."

As they reached home, the first big white snowflakes started to fall. They kept falling all that night and all the next day. It was the first real snowstorm of the year.

In the morning the wind was blowing so fiercely that Wilbur found it hard to walk to the barn where the wood was stored. The wind was so strong it almost knocked him down. He burst through the kitchen door with an armful of wood for the stove, and he told his mother about the wind.

"The thing to do is to lean forward into the wind," she said. "Bend over, and that way you get closer to the ground and you get under the wind."

That night when Wilbur had to make the trip for more wood, he tried his mother's idea. To his surprise it worked! When he was bent over, the wind didn't seem nearly so strong.

After a few days the wind stopped, and now the whole country-side was covered with snow. Wilbur and Orville, with little Kate trailing behind, hurried to the Big Hill not far from the house.

Orville's schoolmates were all there with their sleds. It was a good hill to coast down because no roads came anywhere near it, and even if they had, it wouldn't have mattered. This was 1878 and there were no automobiles. Horse-drawn sleighs traveled the roads in winter. The horses had bells fastened to their collars, and as they jogged along the bells rang and you could hear them a mile away.

Most of the boys had their own sleds; not the flexible fliers boys have now, but old-fashioned sleds with two wooden runners. No one ever thought of owning a "bought" sled. In those days a boy's father made a sled for him.

The boys who had sleds of their own let Wilbur and Orville ride down the hill with them. Ed Sines and Chauncey Smith and Johnny Morrow and Al Johnston all owned sleds, but they liked to race one another down the long hill. When this happened Wilbur and Orville just had to stand there and watch. Late that afternoon the boys came home, with little Kate trailing behind, and their mother noticed that they were very quiet. She was wise as well as very pretty, and she soon found out why they were unhappy.

"Why doesn't Father build us a sled?" Wilbur blurted out.

"But Father is away, Will," his mother said gently. "And you know how busy he is when he is at home. He has to write stories for the church paper and he has to write sermons. Now suppose we build a sled together."

Wilbur laughed. "Whoever heard of anyone's mother building a sled?"

"You just wait," his mother said. "We'll build a better sled than Ed Sines has. Now get me a pencil and a piece of paper."

"You goin' to build a sled out of paper?" Orville asked in amazement.

"Just wait," she repeated.

"Get It Right on Paper"

Will and Orv brought their mother a pencil and paper, and she went to the minister's desk and found a ruler. Then she sat down at the kitchen table. "First we'll draw a picture of the sled," she said.

"What good is a picture of a sled?" Orville asked.

"Now Orville, watch Mother." She picked up the ruler in one hand and the pencil in the other.

"We want one like Ed Sines has," Orville said.

"When you go coasting, how many boys will Ed Sines's sled hold?" she asked.

"Two," Wilbur said.

"We'll make this one big enough to hold three," she said. "Maybe you can take Kate along sometimes." The outline of a sled began to appear on the paper. As she drew it she talked. "You see, Ed's sled is about four feet long. I've seen it often enough. We'll make this one five feet long. Now, Ed's sled is about a foot off the ground, isn't it?"

Orville nodded, his eyes never leaving the drawing that was taking shape. It was beginning to look like a sled now, but not like the sleds the other boys had.

"You've made it too low," Will said.

"You want a sled that's faster than Ed's sled, don't you?" His mother smiled. "Well, Ed's sled is at least a foot high. Our sled will be lower—closer to the ground. It won't meet so much wind resistance."

"Wind resistance?" It was the first time Wilbur had ever heard the expression. He looked blankly at his mother.

"Remember the blizzard last week?" she asked. "Remember when you went out to the woodshed and the wind was so strong you could hardly walk to the shed? I told you to lean over, and on the next trip to the woodshed you did. When you came back with an armful of wood you laughed and said, 'Mother, I leaned 'way forward and got under the wind.' You were closer to the ground and you were able to lessen the wind resistance. Now, the closer to the ground our sled is the less wind resistance there will be, and the faster it will go."

"Wind resistance . . . wind resistance," Wilbur repeated, and maybe the airplane was born in that moment. Certainly neither Will nor Orville Wright ever forgot that first lesson in speed.

"How do you know about these things, Mother?" Wilbur asked.

"You'd be surprised how much mothers know, Will." She laughed. She didn't tell the boys that when she was a little girl at school her best subject had been arithmetic. It just came naturally to her. It was the same when she went to high school. And when she went to college, algebra and geometry were her best subjects. That was why she knew all about things like "wind resistance."

resistance—*used to slow down an object*

50

Finally she finished the drawing. The boys leaned over the table to look at it. This sled was going to be longer than Ed's sled and much narrower. Ed's sled was about three feet wide. This one looked as if it would be only half that wide.

"You made it narrow," Wilbur said shrewdly, "to make it faster. The narrower it is, the less wind resistance."

"That's right." His mother nodded. "Now let's put down the exact length of the runners and the exact width of the sled."

"But that's only a paper sled," Orville protested.

"If you get it right on paper," she said calmly, "it'll be right when you build it. Always remember that."

"'If you get it right on paper, it'll be right when you build it,'" Wilbur repeated, and his mother looked at him sharply. Sometimes Will seemed older than his eleven years. Little Orville was quick to give you an answer to anything, but as often as not he'd forget the answer right away. When Will learned something he never forgot it.

"Mother, you make all your clothes," Wilbur said thoughtfully. "You always make a drawing first."

"We call that the pattern," his mother said. "I draw and then cut out a pattern that's exactly the size of the dress I am going to make. And . . ."

"If the pattern is right, it'll be right when you make the dress," he finished. She nodded.

"Now you two boys get started on your sled." She smiled. "There are plenty of planks out in the barn. Find the very lightest ones. Don't use planks with knots in them. You saw the planks to the right size, Will—don't let Orville touch the saw."

"May we use Father's tools?" Wilbur asked breathlessly.

His mother nodded. "I don't think your father will
mind. I know you'll be careful with them. Just follow the
drawing exactly," she warned once more.

The two boys, followed by little Kate, hurried out to the
barn. Both realized that this was an important occasion.
Wilbur always chopped the wood for the stove when his
father was away, but he had never been allowed to use the
gleaming tools that lay in his father's tool chest.

Three days later their sled was finished. They pulled
it out of the barn and asked their mother to inspect it.
She had her tape measure with her and she measured it.
The runners were exactly the length she had put down in
her drawing. In fact, the boys had followed every direction she had given them. The runners gleamed. Orville
had polished them with sandpaper until they were as
smooth as silk.

"We thought of one other thing, Mother," Will said.
"We found some old candles in the woodshed. We rubbed
the runners with the candles. See how smooth they are?"

Mrs. Wright nodded. She had forgotten to tell the
boys that, but they'd thought it out for themselves. "Now
try your sled," she told them.

Followed by Kate, the boys dragged their new sled
to the hill only half a mile away where their pals were
coasting. They looked at the new sled in amazement. It
was long and very narrow. It looked as though it wouldn't
hold anyone. The runners were thin compared to those
on their own sleds.

"Who made that for you?" Ed Sines asked.

"Mother showed us how," Wilbur said proudly. Some of the boys laughed. Whoever heard of a boy's mother knowing how to make a sled?

"It looks as if it would fall apart if you sat on it," Al Johnston said, and he laughed too.

"Come on, we'll race you down the hill," another cried out.

"All right, two on each sled," Wilbur said. He wasn't a bit afraid. He was sure the drawing had been right, and because he and Orv had followed the drawing, he knew that the sled was right.

They lined the four sleds up. Will and Orv sat on their sled, but it didn't "fall apart." Suddenly Wilbur got an idea.

"Get up, Orv," he said. "Now lie down on the sled . . . that's it . . . spread your legs a bit." Will then flopped down on top of his brother. "Less wind resistance this way," he whispered.

"Give us all a push," Ed Sines yelled.

And then they were off. It was an even start. The four sleds gathered speed, for at the top the slope was steep. Will looked to the right. Then to the left. He brushed the stinging snow out of his eyes but he couldn't see the other sleds. He looked behind. They were straggling along, twenty and now thirty feet in back of him. The new sled skimmed along, the runners singing happily. Both Will and Orv felt a strange thrill of excitement. They approached the bottom of the long hill. The other sleds were far, far behind now.

Usually when the sleds reached the bottom of the hill they slowed down abruptly and stopped. But not this

sled. It kept on; its momentum carried it on and on a hundred yards farther than any of the other sleds had ever reached. Finally it stopped.

Shaking with excitement, Will and Orv stood up.

"We flew down the hill, Orv," Will said breathlessly.

"We flew," Orv repeated.

Now Ed and Al and Johnny ran up, excited at what had happened. No sled had gone so far or so fast as the one Will and Orv had built.

"You *flew* down the hill," Ed Sines gasped. "Let me try it?"

Wilbur looked at Orv, and some secret message seemed to pass between them. They had built this sled together, and it was the best sled there was. They'd always work together building things.

momentum—*the force that keeps an object moving*

"Orv," Will said, "I've got an idea. This sled can do everything but steer. Maybe we can make a rudder for it. Then we can make it go to the right or to the left."

"We'll get Mother to draw one," Orv said.

"We'll draw one, you and I," Wilbur said. "We can't run to Mother every time we want to make something."

By now little Kate had come running down the hill.

"You promised," she panted. "You said you'd take me for a ride."

"Come on, Kate." Will laughed. "The three of us will coast down once. And then you can try it, Ed."

They trudged up the hill, pulling the sled. Two words kept singing in Wilbur's ears. "We flew . . . we flew . . . we flew. . . ."

The Flying Machine

Kitty Hawk hadn't changed much. William Tate was a little older but no busier than he had been on the Wright brothers' first visit. He helped them build a shed to protect their glider and its engine from the storms that occasionally swept over the sand dunes. Then Will and Orv gave him the job of bringing firewood every morning. They paid him a dollar a day for that.

All day long they worked on their glider and their engine. It was a funny-looking thing, and when the men from the life-saving station walked over to look at it they shook their heads.

"You really going to make this thing fly?" one of them asked Wilbur.

"Maybe, maybe," Will said.

---

rudder—*used to steer or change directions*
glider—*a light aircraft that glides in the wind*

"How long you been working on this?" another asked.

"All our lives," Orville said, and that was the truth.

Their first flying machine—the word airplane wasn't used then—didn't have wheels. It had skids (something like skis). Will and Orv built two wooden tracks and laid them out on the sand. They would launch their flying machine from this track. They tested the engine again and again. It made a lot of noise and it shook the whole glider, but it was well fastened to the lower wing and it wouldn't fly off. At least, they hoped it wouldn't.

"I think we can try it today," Will said casually on the morning of December 17, 1903. Will probably didn't realize that forever and ever, boys and girls in school would learn that date. December 17, 1903, is one of the most important dates in history.

"We're as ready as we ever will be," Orv said just as casually.

Outwardly they were calm, but they were human, and you can be sure that they were excited inside. They tossed a coin to decide which one would try the machine first. Orv won.

"I'm going to fly today," Orv whispered to himself. "I'm going to be the first man in the world to fly."

There were only five people out near the lonely sand dune to watch the flying machine try to get into the air, and not one of them thought it could do it. One of the five was a sixteen-year-old boy named Johnny Moore, whose father was a fisherman. They started up the engine. Orv climbed onto the lower wing. Wilbur steadied the glider, which was vibrating terrifically.

"You ready, Orv?" Wilbur shouted.

"All set," Orv yelled back.

"Let her go," Wilbur cried, and Orv released the lever that made the propellers "bite" into the air. The glider started to move along the track slowly . . . a bit quicker . . . and then, just as it reached the end of the track the front of the glider rose up, the rest followed, and the flying machine was in the air. It rose to ten feet. It was flying. It sped along in the air. Wilbur, usually calm, was trembling with joy. Orville was actually flying. The flying machine went a hundred feet and then it glided down gracefully to the sand.

Orville tumbled out of the first machine that had ever really flown.

"We did it, Will," he said, his voice shaky.

"We can fly," Wilbur said with awe. "We can fly."

"How long was I up?" Orv asked.

"Twenty seconds," Will said. "Now let me try it."

Wilbur flew a hundred and seventy-five feet and then let the machine come down. Orville tried again and came down after about fifteen seconds.

"Will, see how far you can fly it," Orville suggested when Wilbur took his position to try again. Will nodded. Once again the flying machine was launched. It rose about twenty feet and then Wilbur leveled it off. Looking down he saw the sand dunes flying past him. The flying

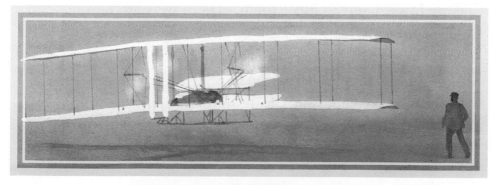

machine kept on and on. This was a real flight. Two startled seagulls flew alongside, screaming shrilly. What new kind of bird was this? When Wilbur had flown eight hundred feet a draft of down air forced the flying machine to land.

"You were up there fifty-nine seconds," Orv shouted as Wilbur climbed down from the lower wing.

"Next time we'll stay up fifty-nine minutes," Wilbur said with a laugh.

"Let's send a telegram to Father," Orv said.

The four men and the sixteen-year-old boy who had watched the first flight of an airplane came running up to shake hands with the two brothers. Even now they could hardly believe their eyes. They had seen a heavy, ungainly looking glider with a heavy engine actually rise from the ground and fly. No one else in history had ever seen anything like this before.

Wilbur and Orville hurried to send a telegram to their father and to Kate. Back home, the bishop and his daughter read the telegram with shining eyes. They ran to the shop to tell Charley Taylor about it. He wasn't a bit excited.

"Knew they'd do it all along," he said calmly.

A week later Wilbur and Orville came home. There was no brass band to meet them. There were no newspapermen at the station. Bishop Wright and Kate were the only ones to welcome them.

"We flew, Kate," Orv said happily.

"They don't believe it," Kate said angrily.

"Who doesn't believe it?" Will asked.

---

ungainly—*awkward and clumsy*

"The newspapers, the people, even the neighbors," Kate said bitterly.

"First they think we're crazy," Orv said. "Now they think we're liars."

"Don't worry, boys," their father said. "I once told you that God had big plans for you two. I was right. No one can interfere with His plans, my sons. He gave you something special that allowed you to be the first two men in history to fly. Let people laugh."

"We'll show them," Orv said grimly.

Character Theme—Aspirations & Initiative

Time to Think

1. Describe Wilbur and Orville's mother.
2. What did Mrs. Wright teach Wilbur about the wind?
3. How was the Wright brothers' sled different from the other boys' sleds?
4. What did Orville mean when he said that he and Wilbur had been working on a flying machine all of their lives?
5. What good advice did Mr. Wright give Wilbur and Orville when people laughed at them and their flying machine?

Try, Try Again

T. H. Palmer

'Tis a reason you should heed,
Try, try again;
If at first you don't succeed,
Try, try again;
Then your courage should appear,
For, if you will persevere,
You will conquer, never fear,
Try, try again.

Sergeant York— Tennessee Marksman

Col. Red Reeder (adapted)

In 1918, in the Argonne Forest of France, a redheaded, rawboned corporal in the 82nd Division performed one of the most famous feats of arms in American military history. His name was Alvin C. York, and he was a soldier who, at the outset, had not wanted to fight at all. When he received the letter saying that he had been drafted, York wrote in protest to President Woodrow Wilson, saying that he was a leader in his church. Alvin York never received an answer from Mr. Wilson, so he had to choose between being classed as a draft-dodger or reporting to the Army. This was a soul-searching time for York, but he finally reported for his Army physical examination, and the doctor passed him quickly.

The next problem developed at Camp Gordon, Georgia, where the 82nd was in training. York, a huge hulk of a fellow, could lie on the firing point at the range with his

---

rawboned—*thin, with bones that stick out*   outset—*beginning*
feats—*courageous acts*

1903 Springfield rifle and send bullets cracking down the range into the bull's-eye. The distances were 200, 300, and 500 yards, and it made no difference to him whether he was firing from a standing, prone, or kneeling position.

But when York was asked to fire at silhouette targets representing men, he balked. He requested permission to see his company commander, Captain E. C. B. Danforth. "Sir, I am doing wrong," Private York said to the captain. "Practicing to kill people is against my religion."

Captain Danforth reasoned with York, giving him every argument he could think of to convince him that he should fight for his country, but York would not be budged. He was determined to leave the Army, even though it meant work at hard labor in a detention camp for conscientious objectors.

The captain asked the battalion commander, Major George E. Buxton, of Providence, Rhode Island, a student of the Bible, to talk with York, and the major discussed the matter with the blue-eyed Tennessean for the better part of three days. Buxton pointed out that the great heroes and leaders of the Old Testament were staunch men who fought for their homes and people. York kept saying, "But the Old Book says, 'Thou shalt not kill.'"

Finally Major Buxton sent York back to his home on the wild Wolf River on leave and told him to think the problem through carefully.

In two weeks Alvin York was back. He looked peaceful, and said he was ready to fight.

---

prone—*lying face down*
balked—*stopped and refused to continue*
conscientious objectors—*those who refuse to serve in the military for religious reasons*

battalion—*a large group of soldiers made up of more than one unit*

Thirteen months later, in Argonne, York was a corporal in a platoon that had been raked by German machine guns. The platoon leader lay dead; so did the noncommissioned officers—every one, that is, except York. The remaining privates were frightened.

This was a terrible moment. Corporal York and seven privates lay flat on their stomachs in shell holes, surrounded by dead and wounded Americans. Overhead, bullets from a German machine gun whip cracked through the air. There seemed to be no help for the American platoon. But after several minutes, York located the position of the enemy machine gun. And while the gunners were searching for other targets, York saw his chance. Scrambling to his feet, he shouted, "Follow me!"

Alvin York and his little group ran forward, firing their weapons. They stopped the Germans at the gun, but they had no time to confer about their next action because approximately thirty-five other machine guns opened up on them. Again York and his men threw themselves down, taking refuge in shell holes and behind logs. The roar of the machine-gun battery sounded like a gang of riveters working on steel.

When the fire slackened, York saw that the line of machine-gun nests was about fifty yards away. He called to his men. No one answered. York decided that his salvation lay in carefully firing his rifle.

The first thing he did was to squirm to a better firing position. Then, squinting through the peep sight of his

---

platoon—*two or more sections of troops led by one officer*
raked—*subjected to heavy gunfire*
noncommissioned officers—*men who joined the military as privates and were promoted*

battery—*artillery unit*
riveters—*those who hammer metal bolts*

rifle, he squeezed the trigger. The bolt of his .30 caliber rifle flew back and forth as if it were power operated. He shot twelve enemy gunners in succession. Suddenly, from another direction, six German soldiers charged him, one behind the other, bayonets fixed. York shot them, too. Later, his explanatory statement amused Americans everywhere. "I used an old turkey-shooting trick," he said, with his customary drawl. "It came to me that if I shot the lead ones first, the others could hide behind their bodies like behind a log. If you shoot the hind turkey, the ones in front won't fly because they don't know the tail one's been hit."

When they saw the results of York's amazing marksmanship, 4 German officers and 128 German soldiers surrendered to him. A division inspector in the vicinity checked Alvin York's feat; shortly thereafter Captain Danforth promoted York to sergeant.

York's shooting and his solo attack captured the imagination of the Allied world and made him one of the top heroes of the First World War. Ferdinand Foch, who commanded the French, British, and American armies in France, told him, "What you did was the greatest thing accomplished by any private soldier in all the armies of Europe."

---

vicinity—*the surrounding area*   **Foch** (fôsh)

In February, 1919, the 28,000 soldiers of the 82nd Division paraded before General Charles Summerall, himself a battlefield hero. York carried the division's flag. At the end of the ceremony, Summerall gathered the men about him in a hollow square and, with York out in front, the general thanked him for his services to the United States. Next, General Pershing, AEF commander, came to the division to add his appreciation for its effort and to thank York personally.

A few weeks later, under a lead-gray sky, the division again paraded, this time for its own commanding general, George B. Duncan. It was a bitter day, a setting reminiscent of the sacrifice of the 82nd. The division had lost over 7,000 officers and soldiers—killed, wounded, or missing in action. After the bands played the national anthem, General Duncan placed a blue ribbon about Alvin York's neck. Suspended from it was the Medal of Honor.

When Sergeant York returned to the United States with the men of his division he was met at the dock by representatives of many commercial and business enterprises. The agents were ready with all sorts of plans that would bring him ready cash, but he answered each simply, "Uncle Sam's uniform's not for sale."

Everyone wanted to see the hero. At the New York Stock Exchange he was carried about the floor on the shoulders of businessmen, and on Capitol Hill Congress gave him a standing ovation. What York did and said made front-page news; people expected he would tour the country.

AEF—*American Expeditionary Force; American troops sent to Europe during World War I*
reminiscent—*reminding one of the past*

ovation—*lengthy applause*

But he was not interested in fame. When questioned at dinners about his amazing exploit, York would blush and answer in his soft drawl, "It was nothin'. I wanted to do the best I could." After he returned to Tennessee he talked of his prolonged questioning by reporters. "I was sorter feeling like a red fox circling when the hounds are after it. They asked me that many questions that I kinder got tired inside my head and wanted to light out and do some hiking."

To keep busy, the big, broad-shouldered mountaineer served as superintendent of Cumberland State Park, near Crossville, Tennessee, and in his spare time he took to the fields and woods with friends to hunt quail and turkey.

When he died in 1964, millions of words were written about him. President Lyndon Johnson said, "Sergeant Alvin C. York stood as a symbol of American courage and sacrifice for almost half a century."

The President designated General Matthew B. Ridgway, former chief of staff of the United States Army and a World War II leader of the 82nd Division, as his personal representative at the funeral. In the Wolf Run Cemetery, beside the flag-covered casket, stood Governor Clement of Tennessee, General Ridgway, York's five sons and two daughters, and relatives. Riflemen fired three volleys over the grave, and the shots echoed and re-echoed through the hills that York loved. A bugler sounded "Taps." An American Legion Honor Guard and York's devoted friends saluted the memory of the simple man whose name had become, within his own lifetime, a synonym for bravery.

---

exploit—*heroic act*

Time to Think

1. How did Alvin York feel about being drafted?
2. How was York able to shoot all six of the soldiers who charged him?
3. How was York honored for his bravery?
4. How did York feel about his fame?
5. What did York do when he returned home?

An Early American Orphanage

Louisa May Alcott

"Please, sir, is this Plumfield?" asked a ragged boy of the man who opened the great gate at which the bus left him.

"Yes, who sent you?"

"Mr. Laurence. I have got a letter for the lady."

"All right; go up to the house, and give it to her; she'll see to you, little chap."

The man spoke pleasantly, and the boy went on, feeling much cheered by the words. Through the soft spring rain that fell on sprouting grass and budding trees, Nat saw a large square house before him—a hospitable-looking house, with an old-fashioned porch, wide steps, and lights shining in many windows. Neither curtains nor shutters hid the cheerful glimmer; and, pausing a moment before he rang, Nat saw many little shadows dancing on the walls, heard the pleasant hum of young voices, and felt that it was hardly possible that the light and warmth and comfort within could be for a homeless "little chap" like him.

"I hope the lady *will* see to me," he thought; and gave a timid rap with the great bronze knocker, which was a jovial griffin's head.

A rosy-faced maid opened the door, and smiled as she took the letter which he silently offered. She seemed used to receiving strange boys, for she pointed to a seat in the hall, and said with a nod: "Sit there and drip on the mat a bit, while I take this in to missis."

Nat found plenty to amuse him while he waited, and stared about him curiously, enjoying the view, yet glad to do so unobserved in the dusky recess by the door.

The house seemed swarming with boys, who were beguiling the rainy twilight with all sorts of amusements. There were boys everywhere, "upstairs and downstairs and in the lady's chamber," apparently, for various open doors showed pleasant groups of big boys, little boys, and middle-sized boys in all stages of evening relaxation, not to say effervescence. Two large rooms on the right were evidently schoolrooms, for desks, maps, blackboards, and books were scattered about. An open fire burned on the hearth, and several indolent lads lay on their backs before it, discussing a new cricket ground with such animation that their boots waved in the air. A tall youth was practicing on the flute in one corner, quite undisturbed by the racket all about him. Two or three others were jumping

---

griffin—*the image of a beast with the body of a lion and the head and wings of an eagle*
recess—*a hollow, secluded place*

beguiling—*passing time*
effervescence—*high spirits*
indolent—*lazy*

over the desks, pausing, now and then, to get their breath, and laugh at the droll sketches of a little wag who was caricaturing the whole household on a blackboard.

In the room on the left a long supper table was seen, set forth with great pitchers of new milk, piles of brown and white bread, and perfect stacks of the shiny ginger-bread so dear to boyish souls. A flavor of toast was in the air, also suggestions of baked apples, very tantalizing to one hungry little nose and stomach.

The hall, however, presented the most inviting prospect of all, for a brisk game of tag was going on in the upper entry. One landing was devoted to marbles, the other to checkers, while the stairs were occupied by a boy reading, a girl singing a lullaby to her doll, two puppies, a kitten, and a constant succession of small boys sliding down the banisters, to the great detriment of their clothes and danger to their limbs.

So absorbed did Nat become in this exciting race, that he ventured farther and farther out of his corner. When one very lively boy came down so swiftly that he could not stop himself, but fell off the banisters, with a crash that would have broken any head but one rendered nearly as hard as a cannon ball by eleven years of constant bump-ing, Nat forgot himself, and ran up to the fallen rider, expecting to find him half dead. The boy, however, only winked rapidly for a second, then lay calmly looking up at the new face with a surprised, "Hullo!"

"Hullo!" returned Nat, not knowing what else to say, and thinking that form of reply both brief and easy.

---

droll—*comical*
wag—*a witty person*
caricaturing—*drawing funny pictures*

detriment—*damage*
rendered—*made to be*

"Are you a new boy?" asked the recumbent youth, without stirring.

"Don't know yet."

"What's your name?"

"Nat Blake."

"Mine's Tommy Bangs; come up and have a go, will you?" and Tommy stood up on his legs like one suddenly remembering the duties of hospitality.

"Guess I won't until I see whether I'm going to stay or not," returned Nat, feeling the desire to stay increase every moment.

"I say, Demi, here's a new one. Come and see to him," and the lively Thomas returned to his sport with unabated relish.

---

recumbent—*relaxing*   **unabated relish**—*enjoyment that does not lessen*

At his call, the boy reading on the stairs looked up with a pair of big brown eyes. After an instant's pause, as if a little shy, he put the book under his arm, and came soberly down to greet the newcomer, who found something very attractive in the pleasant face of this slender, mild-eyed boy.

"Have you seen Aunt Jo?" he asked, as if that was some sort of important ceremony.

"I haven't seen anybody yet but you boys; I'm waiting," answered Nat.

"Did Uncle Laurie send you?" proceeded Demi, politely but gravely.

"Mr. Laurence did."

"He is Uncle Laurie; and he always sends nice boys."

Nat looked gratified at the remark, and smiled in a way that made his thin face very pleasant. He did not know what to say next, so the two stood staring at one another in friendly silence, until the little girl came up with her doll in her arms. She was very like Demi, only not so tall, and had a rounder, rosier face, and blue eyes.

"This is my sister Daisy," announced Demi, as if presenting a rare and precious creature.

The children nodded to one another; and the little girl's face dimpled with pleasure, as she said, pleasantly: "I hope you'll stay. We have such good times here; don't we, Demi?"

"Of course, we do; that's what Aunt Jo has Plumfield for."

"It seems a very nice place indeed," observed Nat, feeling that he must respond to these amiable young persons.

"It's the nicest place in the world; isn't it, Demi?" said Daisy, who evidently regarded her brother as an authority on all subjects.

"No, I think Greenland, where the icebergs and seals are, is more interesting. But I'm fond of Plumfield, and it *is* a very nice place to be in," returned Demi, who was interested just now in a book on Greenland. He was about to offer to show Nat the pictures and explain them, when the maid returned, saying, with a nod toward the parlor door: "All right; you are to stop."

"I'm glad; now come to Aunt Jo." And Daisy took him by the hand with a pretty protecting air, which made Nat feel at home at once.

Demi returned to his beloved book, while his sister led the newcomer into a back room, where a stout gentleman was frolicking with two little boys on the sofa, and a thin lady was just finishing the letter which she seemed to have been rereading.

"Here he is, Aunty!" cried Daisy.

"So this is my new boy? I am glad to see you, my dear, and hope you'll be happy here," said the lady, drawing him to her, and stroking back the hair from his forehead with a kind hand and a motherly look, which made Nat's lonely little heart yearn toward her.

She was not at all handsome, but she had a merry sort of face, that never seemed to have forgotten certain childish ways and looks, any more than her voice and manner had. These things, hard to describe but very plain to see and feel, made her a genial, comfortable kind of person, easy to get on with, and generally "jolly," as boys would say. She saw the little tremble of Nat's lips as she smoothed his hair, and her keen eyes grew softer, but she only drew the shabby figure nearer, and said, laughing: "I am Mother

genial—*friendly and kind*

73

Bhaer; that gentleman is Father Bhaer; and these are the two little Bhaers. Come here, boys, and see Nat."

The three wrestlers obeyed at once; and the stout man, with a chubby child on each shoulder, came up to welcome the new boy. Rob and Teddy merely grinned at him, but Mr. Bhaer shook hands, and pointing to a low chair near the fire, said, in a cordial voice: "There is a place all ready for thee, my son; sit down and dry thy wet feet at once."

"Wet? so they are! My dear, off with your shoes this minute, and I'll have some dry things ready for you in a jiffy," cried Mrs. Bhaer, bustling about so energetically that Nat found himself in the cozy little chair, with dry socks and warm slippers on his feet, before he could have had time to say Jack Robinson, if he had wanted to try. He said, "Thank you, ma'am," instead; and said it so gratefully that Mrs. Bhaer's eyes grew soft again, and she said something merry, because she felt so tender, which was a way she had.

"These are Tommy Bangs's slippers; but he never will remember to put them on in the house; so he shall not have them. They are too big; but that's all the better; you can't run away from us so fast as if they fitted."

"I don't want to run away, ma'am." And Nat spread his grimy little hands before the comfortable blaze, with a long sigh of satisfaction.

"That's good! Now I am going to toast you well, and try to get rid of that ugly cough. How long have you had it, dear?" asked Mrs. Bhaer as she rummaged in her big basket for a strip of flannel.

---

cordial—*warm and sincere*

"All winter. I got cold, and it wouldn't get better, somehow."

"No wonder, living in that damp cellar with hardly a rag to his poor dear back!" said Mrs. Bhaer, in a low tone to her husband, who was looking at the boy with a skillful pair of eyes, that marked the thin temples and feverish lips, as well as the hoarse voice and frequent fits of coughing that shook the bent shoulders under the patched jacket.

"Robin, my man, trot up to Nursey, and tell her to give thee the cough bottle and the liniment," said Mr. Bhaer, after his eyes had exchanged telegrams with his wife's.

Nat looked a little anxious at the preparations, but forgot his fears in a hearty laugh, when Mrs. Bhaer whispered to him, with a droll look:

"Hear my rogue Teddy trying to cough. The syrup I'm going to give you has honey in it; and he wants some."

Little Ted was red in the face with his exertions by the time the bottle came, and was allowed to suck the spoon, after Nat had manfully taken a dose, and had the bit of flannel put about his throat.

These first steps toward a cure were hardly completed, when a great bell rang, and a loud tramping through the hall announced supper. Bashful Nat quaked at the thought of meeting many strange boys, but Mrs. Bhaer held out her hand to him, and Rob said, patronizingly, "Don't be 'fraid; I'll take care of you."

A Very Special Talent

Twelve boys, six on a side, stood behind their chairs, prancing with impatience to begin, while the tall flute-playing youth was trying to curb their ardor. But no one sat down until Mrs. Bhaer was in her place behind the teapot, with Teddy on her left, and Nat on her right.

"This is our new boy, Nat Blake. After supper you can say, How do you do? Gently, boys, gently."

As she spoke every one stared at Nat, and then whisked into their seats, trying to be orderly, and failing utterly. The Bhaers did their best to have the lads behave well at mealtimes, and generally succeeded pretty well, for their rules were few and sensible, and the boys, knowing that they tried to make things easy and happy, did their best to obey. But there *are* times when hungry boys cannot be repressed without real cruelty, and Saturday evening, after a half-holiday, was one of those times.

"Dear little souls, do let them have one day in which they can howl and racket and frolic, to their hearts' content. A holiday isn't a holiday without plenty of freedom and fun; and they shall have full swing once a week," Mrs. Bhaer used to say, when prim people wondered why banister-sliding, pillow fights, and all manner of jovial

---

patronizingly—*in a manner of superiority*   ardor—*enthusiasm*

games were allowed under the once decorous roof of Plumfield.

It did seem at times as if this very roof was in danger of flying off; but it never did, for a word from Father Bhaer could at any time produce a lull, and the lads had learned that liberty must not be abused. So, in spite of many dark predictions, the school flourished, and manners and morals were insinuated, without the pupils exactly knowing how it was done.

Nat found himself very well off behind the tall pitchers, with Tommy Bangs just around the corner, and Mrs. Bhaer close by, to fill up plate and mug as fast as he could empty them.

"Who is that boy next to the girl down at the other end?" whispered Nat to his young neighbor under cover of a general laugh.

"That's Demi Brooke. Mr. Bhaer is his uncle."

"What a queer name!"

"His real name is John, but they call him Demi-John, because his father is John too. That's a joke, don't you see?" said Tommy, kindly explaining. Nat did not see, but politely smiled, and asked, with interest: "Isn't he a very nice boy?"

"I bet you he is; knows lots and reads like anything."

"Who is the big one next to him?"

"Oh, that's Stuffy Cole. His name is George, but we call him Stuffy 'cause he eats so much. The little fellow next to Father Bhaer is his boy Rob, and then there's big Franz his nephew; he teaches some, and kind of sees to us."

---

decorous—*mannerly*   insinuated—*introduced gradually*

"He plays the flute, doesn't he?" asked Nat as Tommy rendered himself speechless by putting a whole baked apple into his mouth at one blow.

Tommy nodded, and said, sooner than one would have imagined possible under the circumstances: "Oh, doesn't he, though? and we do gymnastics to music. I like a drum myself, and mean to learn as soon as ever I can."

"I like a fiddle best. I can play one too," said Nat, getting confidential on this attractive subject.

"Can you?" said Tommy as he stared over the rim of his mug with round eyes, full of interest. "Mr. Bhaer's got an old fiddle, and he'll let you play on it if you want to."

"Could I? Oh, I would like it ever so much. You see I used to go around fiddling with my father, and another man, until he died."

"Wasn't that fun?" cried Tommy, much impressed.

"No, it was horrid; so cold in winter, and hot in summer. And I got tired; and they were cross sometimes, and I didn't have enough to eat." Nat paused to take a generous bite of gingerbread, as if to assure himself that the hard times were over; and then he added, regretfully: "But I did love my little fiddle, and I miss it. Nicolo took it away when father died, and wouldn't have me any longer, 'cause I was sick."

"You'll belong to the band if you play good. See if you don't."

"Do you have a band here?" And Nat's eyes sparkled.

"Guess we do; a jolly band, all boys; and they have concerts and things. You just see what happens tomorrow night."

After this pleasantly exciting remark, Tommy returned to his supper, and Nat sank into a blissful reverie over his full plate.

Mrs. Bhaer had heard all they said, while apparently absorbed in filling mugs, and overseeing little Ted, who was so sleepy that he put his spoon in his eye, nodded like a rosy poppy, and finally fell fast asleep, with his cheek pillowed on a soft bun. Mrs. Bhaer had put Nat next to Tommy, because that roly-poly boy had a frank and social way with him, very attractive to shy persons. Nat felt this, and had made several small confidences during supper, which gave Mrs. Bhaer the key to the new boy's character, better than if she had talked to him herself.

In the letter which Mr. Laurence had sent with Nat, he had said:

Dear Jo,

Here is a case after your own heart. This poor lad is an orphan now, sick and friendless. He has been a street musician; and I found him in a cellar, mourning for his dead father and his lost violin. I think there is something in him, and have a fancy that between us we may give this little man a lift. You cure his overtasked body, Fritz help his neglected mind, and when he is ready I'll see if he is a genius or only a boy with a talent which may earn his bread for him. Give him a trial, for the sake of your own boy.

Teddy

---

reverie—*daydreaming*

"Of course we will!" cried Mrs. Bhaer, as she read the letter. When she saw Nat, she felt at once that, whether he was a genius or not, here was a lonely, sick boy, who needed just what she loved to give, a home and motherly care. But she and Mr. Bhaer observed him quietly; and in spite of ragged clothes, awkward manners, and a dirty face, they saw much about Nat that pleased them. He was a thin, pale boy of twelve, with blue eyes, and a good forehead under the rough, neglected hair; an anxious, scared face, at times, as if he expected hard blows or words; and a sensitive mouth, that trembled when a kind glance fell on him; while a gentle speech called up a look of gratitude, very sweet to see. "Bless the poor dear, he shall fiddle all day long if he likes," said Mrs. Bhaer to herself, as she saw the eager, happy expression on his face when Tommy talked of the band.

So, after supper, when the lads flocked into the schoolroom for more "high jinks," Mrs. Bhaer appeared with a violin in her hand, and, after a word with her husband went to Nat, who sat in a corner watching the scene with intense interest.

"Now, my lad, give us a little tune. We want a violin in our band, and I think you will do it nicely."

She expected that he would hesitate; but he seized the old fiddle at once, and handled it with such loving care, it was plain to see that music was his passion.

"I'll do the best I can, ma'am," was all he said; and then he drew the bow across the strings, as if eager to hear the dear notes again.

"high jinks"—*loud, playful activity*

There was a great
clatter in the room, but
as if deaf to any sounds
but those he made, Nat
played softly to himself,
forgetting everything in
his delight. It was only
a simple spiritual, such
as street musicians play,
but it caught the ears
of the boys at once, and
silenced them, until they
stood listening with surprise

and pleasure. Gradually they came nearer and nearer,
and Mr. Bhaer came up to watch the boy; for, as if he was
in his element now, Nat played away and never minded
anyone, while his eyes shone, his cheeks reddened, and his
thin fingers flew, as he hugged the old fiddle and made it
speak to all their hearts the language that he loved.

A hearty round of applause rewarded him better than
a shower of pennies, when he stopped and glanced about
him, as if to say: "I've done my best; please like it."

"I say, you do that first rate," cried Tommy, who
considered Nat his protégé.

"You shall be first fiddle in my band," added Franz,
with an approving smile.

Mrs. Bhaer whispered to her husband: "Teddy is right:
there's something in the child." And Mr. Bhaer nodded
his head emphatically, as he clapped Nat on the shoulder,

---

in his element—*doing what he does
best or enjoys most*

protégé—*one who is trained
by another*

saying, heartily: "You play well, my son. Come now and play something which we can sing."

It was the proudest, happiest minute of the poor boy's life when he was led to the place of honor by the piano, and the lads gathered around, never heeding his poor clothes, but eyeing him respectfully, and waiting eagerly to hear him play again.

They chose a song he knew; and after one or two false starts they got going, and violin, flute, and piano led a chorus of boyish voices that made the old roof ring again. It was too much for Nat, more feeble than he knew; and as the final shout died away, his face began to work, he dropped the fiddle, and, turning to the wall, sobbed like a little child.

"My dear, what is it?" asked Mrs. Bhaer, who had been singing with all her might, and trying to keep little Rob from beating time with his boots.

"You are all so kind—and it's so beautiful—I can't help it," sobbed Nat, coughing until he was breathless.

"Come with me, dear; you must go to bed and rest; you are worn out, and this is too noisy a place for you," whispered Mrs. Bhaer. Then she took him away to her own parlor, where she let him cry himself quiet.

After a while she won him over and as he told her all his troubles, she listened to the little story with tears in her own eyes, though it was not a new one to her.

"My child, you *have* got a father and a mother now, and this is home. Don't think of those sad times any more, but get well and happy; and be sure you shall never suffer again, if we can help it. This place is made for all sorts of boys to have a good time in, and to learn how to help themselves and be useful men, I hope. You shall have as much music as you want, only you must get strong first. Now come up to Nursey and have a bath, and then go to bed, and tomorrow we will lay some nice little plans together."

Pillow Fights and Sweet Dreams

Nat held her hand fast in his, but had not a word to say, and let his grateful eyes speak for him, as Mrs. Bhaer led him up to a big room, where they found a stout German woman with a face so round and cheery that it looked like a sort of sun, with the wide frill of her cap for rays.

"This is Nursey Hummel, and she will cut your hair and make you all 'comfy,' as Rob says. That's the bath-room in there; and on Saturday nights we scrub all the little lads first, and pack them away in bed before the big ones get through singing. Now then, Rob, in with you."

As she talked, Mrs. Bhaer had whipped off Rob's clothes and popped him into a long bathtub in the little room opening into the nursery.

There were two tubs, besides foot baths, basins, and all manner of contrivances for cleanliness. Nat was soon luxuriating in the other bath; and while simmering there he watched the performances of the two women, who scrubbed, clean night-gowned, and bundled into bed four or five small boys, who, of course, put up all sorts of capers during the operation, and kept every one in a gale of merriment until they were muffled in their beds.

By the time Nat was washed and done up in a blanket by the fire, while Nursey cut his hair, a new detachment of

---

detachment—*a small group sent on a mission*

boys arrived and were shut into the bathroom, where they made as much splashing and noise as a school of young whales at play.

"Nat had better sleep here, so that if his cough troubles him in the night you can see that he takes a good draught of flax-seed tea," said Mrs. Bhaer, who was flying about like a distracted hen with large brood of lively ducklings.

Nursey approved the plan, finished Nat off with a flannel nightgown, a drink of something warm and sweet, and then tucked him into one of the three little beds standing in the room, where he lay looking like a contented mummy, and feeling that nothing more in the way of luxury could be offered him. Cleanliness in itself was a new and delightful sensation; flannel gowns were unknown comforts in his world; sips of "good stuff" soothed his cough as pleasantly as kind words did his lonely heart; and the feeling that somebody cared for him made that plain room seem a sort of heaven to the homeless child. It was like a cozy dream; and he often shut his eyes to see if it would not vanish when he opened them again. It was too pleasant to let him sleep, and he could not have done so if he had tried, for in a few minutes one of the peculiar institutions of Plumfield was revealed to his astonished but appreciative eyes.

A momentary lull in the aquatic exercises was followed by the sudden appearance of pillows flying in all directions, hurled by white goblins, who came rioting out of their beds. The battle raged in several rooms, all down the upper hall, and even surged at intervals into the nursery, when some hard-pressed warrior took refuge there. No one seemed to mind this explosion in the least; no one forbade it, or even looked surprised. Nursey went on hanging up towels, and Mrs. Bhaer picked out clean clothes, as calmly as if the most perfect order reigned.

Nay, she even chased one daring boy out of the room, and fired after him the pillow he had slyly thrown at her.

"Won't they hurt 'em?" asked Nat, who lay laughing with all his might.

"Oh dear, no! We always allow one pillow fight Saturday night. The cases are changed tomorrow; and it gets up a glow after the boys' baths; so I rather like it myself," said Mrs. Bhaer, busy again among her dozen pairs of socks.

"What a very nice school this is!" observed Nat, in a burst of admiration.

"It's an odd one," laughed Mrs. Bhaer; "but you see we don't believe in making children miserable by too many rules, and too much study. I forbade nightgown parties at first; but, bless you, it was of no use. I could no more keep those boys in their beds than so many jacks in the box. So I made an agreement with them: I was to allow a fifteen-minute pillow fight every Saturday night; and they promised to go properly to bed every other night. I tried it, and it worked well. If they don't keep their word, no frolic; if they do, I just turn the mirrors around, put the lamps in safe places, and let them rampage as much as they like."

"It's a beautiful plan," said Nat, feeling that he should like to join in the battle, but not venturing to propose it the first night. So he lay enjoying the spectacle, which certainly was a lively one.

Tommy Bangs led the assailing party, and Demi defended his own room with a dogged courage, fine to see, collecting pillows behind him as fast as they were thrown, till the besiegers were out of ammunition, when they would charge upon him in a body, and recover their arms. A few slight accidents occurred, but nobody minded, and gave and took sounding thwacks with perfect good humor, while pillows flew like big snowflakes, until Mrs. Bhaer looked at her watch, and called out: "Time is up, boys. Into bed, every man Jack, or pay the forfeit!"

"What is the forfeit?" asked Nat, sitting up in his eagerness to know what happened to those wretches who disobeyed this most peculiar but public-spirited school ma'am.

"Lose their fun next time," answered Mrs. Bhaer. "I give them five minutes to settle down, then put out the lights, and expect order. They are honorable lads, and they keep their word."

That was evident, for the battle ended as abruptly as it began—a parting shot or two, a final cheer, as Demi fired the seventh pillow at the retiring foe, a few challenges for next time, then order prevailed; and nothing but an occasional giggle, or a suppressed whisper, broke the

---

assailing—*attacking*

quiet which followed the Saturday-night frolic, as Mother Bhaer kissed her new boy, and left him to happy dreams of life at Plumfield.

Meet the Author

Louisa May Alcott wrote *Little Women*, one of America's best-loved stories. The book was so popular that readers wanted to hear more about Meg, Jo, Beth, and Amy March, the four "little women" who were really Louisa May and her sisters.

She soon wrote *Little Men, Jo's Boys, Eight Cousins,* and other books. The preceding story is the first chapter of *Little Men.*

Louisa May Alcott (1832–1888) lived most of her life around Boston.

Character Theme—Kindness / Compassion & Gratitude

Time to Think

1. Who sent Nat Blake to Plumfield?
2. What kind of person was Mrs. (Jo) Bhaer?
3. What was Plumfield?
4. What was Nat's talent?
5. How did Nat feel about being at Plumfield?

A Nation's Strength

Ralph Waldo Emerson

Not gold, but only man can make
    A people great and strong;
Men who, for truth and honor's sake
    Stand fast and suffer long.

Brave men who work while others sleep,
    Who dare while others fly—
They build a nation's pillars deep
    And lift them to the sky.

*Give me a man
who will do a day's
work for a day's pay,
who will refuse bribes,
who will not
make up his facts,
and who has
learned his job.*
    —C. S. Lewis

I do the very best I know how—the very best I can. If the end brings me out all right, what is said against me won't amount to anything. If the end brings me out wrong, ten thousand angels swearing I was right would make no difference.
                                                    —*Abraham Lincoln*

Washington's Prayer at Valley Forge

Thomas Fleming

In that dreadful winter at Valley Forge, while General Washington's army was freezing, the British sat smugly in Philadelphia growing fat on American bread and beef, their barracks warmed by American firewood.

Each day the mournful cry rose from our enlisted men's huts: "No meat! no meat!" And Washington himself was filled with an overwhelming sense of helplessness. Only a few months before the Valley Forge encampment, late in 1777, he had exclaimed to a New Jersey leader, Elias Boudinot, that he could not do everything. He was general quartermaster and commissary. Everything, he felt, fell on him, and he was "unequal to the task." His desperation was summed up in the cry he emitted at the end of the year in a letter to the Governor of New Jersey: "Our sick naked; our well naked, our unfortunate men in captivity naked!"

---

smugly—*with a feeling of satisfaction |that mocks another*
quartermaster—*the officer responsible for supplies*
commissary—*a person who is given a special duty by a higher authority*

The painting on these pages depicts an American legend—an unverifiable story handed down by tradition from earlier times. No letter or diary survives to give eyewitness testimony that George Washington prayed that cruel winter at Valley Forge. Still, legends usually incorporate an element of the truth.

As far as we know, George Washington never chopped down a cherry tree in his youth. But he *was* the kind of young man who would unflinchingly admit a mistake. In the same way, this painting bears witness to another thoroughly verifiable aspect of his character—his profound faith that America was a nation under God.

Again and again throughout the War for Independence, Washington testified to this faith. On March 13, 1778, when his Army was emerging from the worst of Valley Forge's travail, he wrote to his favorite chaplain, Rev. Israel Evans:

---

depicts—*shows*

unverifiable—*that which cannot be proven*

"It will ever be the first wish of my heart to aid your pious endeavours to inculcate a due sense of the dependance we ought to place in that all wise and powerful Being on Whom alone our success depends."

From our detailed knowledge of those harrowing months at Valley Forge, it is not difficult to believe that Washington prayed. In the painting, he has obviously been on some sort of military mission—inspecting one of Valley Forge's outposts, perhaps. As he rode back to his starving, freezing soldiers who were struggling to defend the infant United States in spite of their countrymen's apparent indifference, where else could he turn but to God?

So there may have been this moment in the snowy woods. We will never know. But there is no doubt that in the greatness of Washington's character, which looms larger in history than any legend about him, there was a profound sense of humility before that Being Whom he called "the All-powerful Guide and Great Disposer of human events."

---

inculcate—*to teach by repetition*
harrowing—*causing distress*

disposer—*one who sets things in order*

Character Theme—Prayer / Faith
& Integrity

Time to Think

1. What was the condition of Washington's army at Valley Forge?

2. Where does it seem that Washington got his strength to continue during this time?

Boy Wanted

Frank Crane

A boy who stands straight, sits straight, acts straight, and talks straight.

A boy who listens carefully when spoken to, who asks questions when he does not understand, and does not ask questions about things that are none of his business.

A boy whose fingernails are not in mourning, whose ears are clean, whose shoes are polished, whose clothes are neat, whose hair is combed, and whose teeth are well cared for.

A boy who moves quickly and makes as little noise about it as possible.

A boy who whistles in the street but not where he ought to keep still.

A boy who looks cheerful, has a ready smile for everybody, and never sulks.

A boy who is polite to every man and respectful to every woman and girl.

A boy who does not smoke and has no desire to learn how.

A boy who never bullies other boys or allows boys to bully him.

A boy who, when he does not know a thing, says, "I do not know"; and when he has made a mistake says, "I'm sorry"; and, when requested to do anything, immediately says, "I'll try."

A boy who looks you right in the eye and tells the truth every time.

A boy who would rather lose his job or be expelled from school than tell a lie.

A boy who is more eager to know how to speak good English than to talk slang.

A boy who does not want to be "smart" nor in anywise attract attention.

A boy who is eager to read good, wholesome books.

A boy whom other boys like.

A boy who is perfectly at ease in the company of respectable girls.

A boy who is not a goody-goody, or a little Pharisee, but just healthy, happy, and full of life.

A boy who is not sorry for himself and not forever thinking and talking about himself.

A boy who is friendly with his mother and confides more in her than in anyone else.

A boy who makes you feel good when he is around.

This boy is wanted everywhere. The family wants him, the school wants him, the office wants him, the boys and girls want him, and all creation wants him.

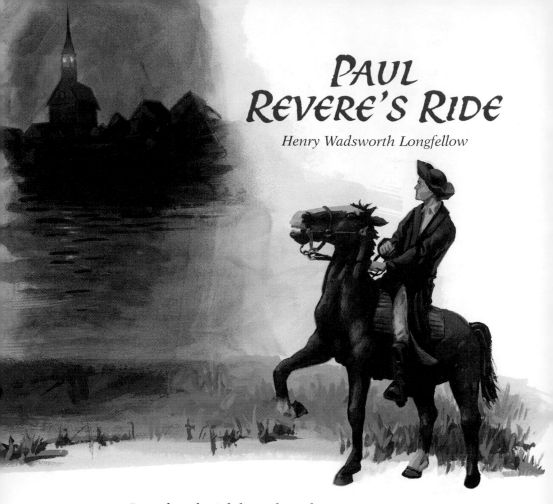

PAUL REVERE'S RIDE

Henry Wadsworth Longfellow

In early colonial days, the only way to get messages to the other colonies was by messengers riding on horseback. In this poem, Henry Wadsworth Longfellow tells how the famous rider named Paul Revere carried an important message from Charlestown to Concord.

Listen, my children, and you shall hear
Of the midnight ride of Paul Revere,
On the eighteenth of April in Seventy-five;
Hardly a man is now alive
Who remembers that famous day and year.

He said to his friend, "If the British march
By land or sea from the town tonight,
Hang a lantern aloft in the belfry arch

Of the North Church tower, as a signal light,—
One, if by land, and two, if by sea;
And I on the opposite shore will be
Ready to ride and spread the alarm
Through every Middlesex village and farm,

For the country folk to be up and to arm."
Then he said, "Good-night!" and with muffled oar
Silently rowed to the Charlestown shore,
Just as the moon rose over the bay,
Where swinging wide at her moorings lay
The *Somerset,* British man-of-war;
A phantom ship, with each mast and spar
Across the moon like a prison bar,
And a huge black hulk, that was magnified
By its own reflection in the tide.

Meanwhile, his friend, through alley and street,
Wanders and watches with eager ears,
Till in the silence around him he hears
The muster of men at the barrack door,
The sound of arms, and the tramp of feet,
And the measured tread of the grenadiers,
Marching down to their boats on the shore.

Beneath, in the churchyard, lay the dead,
In their night encampment on the hill,
Wrapped in silence so deep and still
That he could hear, like a sentinel's tread,
The watchful night wind, as it went
Creeping along from tent to tent,
And seeming to whisper, "All is well!"
A moment only he feels the spell
Of the place and the hour, the secret dread
Of the lonely belfry and the dead;

moorings—*equipment used to hold a ship in place*
barrack—*a place of housing for soldiers*
grenadiers—*British soldiers*

For suddenly all his thoughts are bent
On a shadowy something far away,
Where the river widens to meet the bay,—
A line of black that bends and floats
On the rising tide, like a bridge of boats.

Meanwhile, impatient to mount and ride,
Booted and spurred, with a heavy stride
On the opposite shore walked Paul Revere.
Now he patted his horse's side,
Now gazed at the landscape far and near,
Then, impetuous, stamped the earth,
And turned and tightened his saddle girth;
But mostly he watched with eager search
The belfry tower of the Old North Church,
As it rose above the graves on the hill,
Lonely and spectral and somber and still.
And lo! as he looks, on the belfry's height
A glimmer, and then a gleam of light!
He springs to the saddle, the bridle he turns,
But lingers and gazes, till full on his sight
A second lamp in the belfry burns!

A hurry of hoofs in a village street,
A shape in the moonlight, a bulk in the dark,
And beneath, from the pebbles, in passing, a spark
Struck out by a steed flying fearless and fleet:
That was all! And yet, through the gloom and the light,
The fate of a nation was riding that night;
And the spark struck out by that steed, in his flight,
Kindled the land into flame with its heat.

He has left the village and mounted the steep,
And beneath him, tranquil and broad and deep,
Is the Mystic, meeting the ocean tides;
And under the alders that skirt its edge,

---

impetuous—*full of sudden energy*
spectral—*ghostly*
fleet—*moving rapidly*

Mystic (mĭs'tĭk)—*a river in Massachusetts*
alders—*trees of the birch family*

Now soft on the sand, now loud on the ledge,
Is heard the tramp of the steed as he rides.

It was twelve by the village clock,
When he crossed the bridge into Medford town.
He heard the crowing of the cock,
And the barking of the farmer's dog,
And felt the damp of the river fog,
That rises after the sun goes down.

It was one by the village clock,
When he galloped into Lexington.
He saw the gilded weathercock
Swim in the moonlight as he passed,
And the meetinghouse windows, blank and bare,
Gaze at him with a spectral glare,
As if they already stood aghast
At the bloody work they would look upon.

It was two by the village clock,
When he came to the bridge in Concord town.
He heard the bleating of the flock,
And the twitter of birds among the trees,
And felt the breath of the morning breeze
Blowing over the meadows brown.
And one was safe and asleep in his bed
Who at the bridge would be first to fall,
Who that day would be lying dead,
Pierced by a British musket ball.

You know the rest. In the books you have read,
How the British Regulars fired and fled,—
How the farmers gave them ball for ball,
From behind each fence and farmyard wall,
Chasing the redcoats down the lane,
Then crossing the fields to emerge again
Under the trees at the turn of the road,
And only pausing to fire and load.

So through the night rode Paul Revere;
And so through the night went his cry of alarm
To every Middlesex village and farm,—
A cry of defiance and not of fear,
A voice in the darkness, a knock at the door,
And a word that shall echo forevermore!
For, borne on the night wind of the Past,
Through all our history, to the last,
In the hour of darkness and peril and need,
The people will waken and listen to hear
The hurrying hoof beats of that steed,
And the midnight message of Paul Revere.

borne—*carried*

Henry Wadsworth Longfellow (1807–1882), America's most beloved poet, was born in Portland, Maine. In spite of a number of personal tragedies, Longfellow never lost his cheerful outlook. His poetry is loved for its rhythm and its simplicity of expression. He wrote "Hiawatha's Childhood," "The Children's Hour," "The Village Blacksmith," and "The Arrow and the Song." Longfellow is called the Fireside Poet and the Schoolroom Poet because of his great popularity with people of all ages.

Character Theme—Patriotism & Bravery/Sacrifice

Time to Think

1. On what day did Paul Revere's famous ride take place?
2. For what signal was Paul Revere watching?
3. What war was about to begin?
4. Name some of the towns that Paul Revere warned that night.
5. Why did the author say, "the fate of a nation was riding that night"?

It's American

Mildred L. Jarrell

If it stands for justice,
And the right of it,
If it speaks of goodness,
And the might of it,
If there's challenge, courage, joy
And pride in it . . .
      It's American.

If there's a helping hand,
And words of cheer in it,
If freedom for mankind
Is very clear to it,
If hope, and faith, and love
Are very dear to it . . .
      It's American.

The Blizzard

from The Long Winter
by Laura Ingalls Wilder

Mary and Laura and Carrie were all enjoying school
so much that they were sorry when Saturday and Sunday
interrupted it. They looked forward to Monday. But when
Monday came Laura was cross because her red flannel
underwear was so hot and scratchy.

It made her back itch, and her neck, and her wrists,
and where it was folded around her ankles, under her
stockings and shoe-tops, that red flannel almost drove her
crazy.

At noon she begged Ma to let her change to cooler
underthings. "It's too hot for my red flannels, Ma!" she
protested.

"I know the weather's turned warm," Ma answered
gently "But this is the time of year to wear flannels, and
you would catch cold if you took them off."

Laura went crossly back to school and sat squirming
because she must not scratch. She held the flat geography
open before her, but she wasn't studying. She was trying
to bear the itching flannels and wanting to get home
where she could scratch. The sunshine from the western
windows had never crawled so slowly.

Suddenly there was no sunshine. It went out, as
if someone had blown out the sun like a lamp. The
outdoors was gray, the windowpanes were gray, and at the
same moment a wind crashed against the schoolhouse,

rattling windows and doors and shaking the walls.

Miss Garland started up from her chair. One of the little Beardsley girls screamed and Carrie turned white.

Laura thought, "It happened this way on Plum Creek, the Christmas when Pa was lost." Her whole heart hoped and prayed that Pa was safe at home now.

Teacher and all the others were staring at the windows, where nothing but grayness could be seen. They all looked frightened. Then Miss Garland said, "It is only a storm, children. Go on with your lessons."

The blizzard was scouring against the walls, and the winds squealed and moaned in the stovepipe.

All the heads bent over the books as Teacher had told them to do. But Laura was trying to think how to get home. The schoolhouse was a long way from Main Street, and there was nothing to guide them.

All the others had come from the East that summer. They had never seen a prairie blizzard. But Laura and Carrie knew what it was. Carrie's head was bowed limply above her book, and the back of it, with the white parting between the braids of fine, soft hair, looked small and helpless and frightened.

There was only a little fuel at the schoolhouse. The school board was buying coal, but only one load had been delivered. Laura thought they might outlive the storm in the schoolhouse, but they could not do it without burning all the costly patent desks.

Without lifting her head Laura looked up at Teacher. Miss Garland was thinking and biting her lip. She could not decide to dismiss school because of a storm, but this storm frightened her.

"I ought to tell her what to do," Laura thought. But she could not think what to do. It was not safe to leave the schoolhouse and it was not safe to stay there. Even the twelve patent desks might not last long enough to keep them warm until the blizzard ended. She thought of her wraps and Carrie's, in the entry. Whatever happened she must somehow keep Carrie warm. Already the cold was coming in.

There was a loud thumping in the entry. Every pupil started and looked at the door.

It opened and a man stumbled in. He was bundled in overcoat, cap, and muffler, all solid white with snow driven into the woolen cloth. They could not see who he was until he pulled down the stiffened muffler.

"I came out to get you," he told Teacher.

He was Mr. Foster, the man who owned the ox team and had come in from his claim to stay in town for the winter at Sherwood's, across the street from Teacher's house.

Miss Garland thanked him. She rapped her ruler on the desk and said, "Attention! School is dismissed. You may bring your wraps from the entry and put them on by the stove."

Laura said to Carrie, "You stay here. I'll bring your wraps."

The entry was freezing cold; snow was blowing in between the rough boards of the walls. Laura was chilled before she could snatch her coat and hood from their nail. She found Carrie's and carried the armful into the schoolhouse.

Crowded around the stove, they all put on their wraps and fastened them snugly. Cap Garland did not smile. His blue eyes narrowed and his mouth set straight while Mr. Foster talked.

Laura wrapped the muffler snugly over Carrie's white face and took firm hold of her mittened hand. She told Carrie, "Don't worry, we'll be all right."

"Now, just follow me," said Mr. Foster, taking Teacher's arm. "And keep close together."

He opened the door and led the way with Miss Garland. Mary Power and Minnie each took one of the little Beardsley girls. Ben and Arthur followed them closely, then Laura went out with Carrie into blinding snow. Cap shut the door behind them.

They could hardly walk in the beating, whirling wind. The schoolhouse had disappeared. They could see nothing but swirling whiteness and snow and then a glimpse of each other, disappearing like shadows.

Laura felt that she was smothering. The icy particles of snow whirled scratching into her eyes and smothered her breathing. Her skirts whipped around her, now wrapped so tightly that she could not step, then whirled and lifted to her knees. Suddenly tightening, they made her stumble. She held tightly to Carrie, and Carrie, struggling and staggering, was pulled away by the wind and then flung back against her.

"We can't go on this way," Laura thought. But they had to.

She was alone in the confusion of whirling winds and snow except for Carrie's hand that she must never let go. The winds struck her this way and that. She could not see nor breathe, she stumbled and was falling, then suddenly she seemed to be lifted and Carrie bumped against her. She tried to think. The others must be somewhere ahead. She must walk faster and keep up with them or she and Carrie would be lost. If they were lost on the prairie they would freeze to death.

But perhaps they were all lost. Main Street was only two blocks long. If they were going only a little way to north or south they would miss the block of stores and beyond was empty prairie for miles.

Laura thought they must have gone far enough to reach Main Street, but she could see nothing.

The storm thinned a little. She saw shadowy figures ahead. They were darker gray in the whirling gray whiteness. She went on as fast as she could, with Carrie, until she touched Miss Garland's coat.

They had all stopped. Huddled in their wraps, they stood like bundles close together in the swirling mist. Teacher and Mr. Foster were trying to talk, but the winds confused their shouts so that no one could hear what they said. Then Laura began to know how cold she was.

Her mittened hand was so numb that it hardly felt Carrie's hand. She was shaking all over and deep inside her there was a shaking that she could not stop. Only in her very middle there was a solid knot that ached, and her shaking pulled this knot tighter so that the ache grew worse.

She was frightened about Carrie. The cold hurt too much, Carrie could not stand it. Carrie was so little and thin, she had always been delicate, she could not stand such cold much longer. They must reach shelter soon.

Mr. Foster and Teacher were moving again, going a little to the left. All the others stirred and hurried to follow them. Laura took hold of Carrie with her other hand, that had been in her coat pocket and was not quite so numb, and then suddenly she saw a shadow go by them. She knew it was Cap Garland.

He was not following the others to the left. With hands in his pockets and head bent, he went trudging straight ahead into the storm. A fury of winds thickened the air with snow and he vanished.

Laura did not dare follow him. She must take care of Carrie, and Teacher had told them to follow her. She was sure that Cap was going toward Main Street, but perhaps she was mistaken and she could not take Carrie away from the others.

She kept tight hold of Carrie and hurried to follow Mr. Foster and Teacher as fast as she could. Her chest sobbed for air and her eyes strained open in the icy snow particles that hurt them like sand. Carrie struggled bravely, stumbling and flopping, doing her best to stay on her feet and keep on going. Only for instants when the snow-whirl was thinner could they glimpse the shadows moving ahead of them.

Laura felt that they were going in the wrong direction. She did not know why she felt so. No one could see

106

anything. There was nothing to go by—no sun, no sky, no direction in the winds blowing fiercely from all directions. There was nothing but the dizzy whirling and the cold.

It seemed that the cold and the winds, the noise of the winds and the blinding, smothering, scratching snow, and the effort and the aching, were forever. Pa had lived through three days of a blizzard under the bank of Plum Creek. But there were no creek banks here. Here there was nothing but bare prairie. Pa had told about sheep caught in a blizzard, huddled together under the snow. Some of them had lived. Perhaps people could do that, too. Carrie was too tired to go much farther, but she was too heavy for Laura to carry. They must go on as long as they could, and then . . .

Then, out of the whirling whiteness, something hit her. The hard blow crashed against her shoulder and all through her. She rocked on her feet and stumbled against something solid. It was high, it was hard, it was the corner of two walls. Her hands felt it, her eyes saw it. She had walked against some building.

With all her might she yelled, "Here! Come here! Here's a house!"

All around the house the winds were howling so that at first no one heard her. She pulled the icy stiff muffler from her mouth and screamed into the blinding storm. At last she saw a shadow in it, two tall shadows thinner than the shadowy wall she clung to—Mr. Foster and Teacher. Then other shadows pressed close around her.

No one tried to say anything. They crowded together and they were all there—Mary Power and Minnie, each with a little Beardsley girl, and Arthur Johnson and Ben

Woodworth with the small Wilmarth boys. Only Cap Garland was missing.

They followed along the side of that building till they came to the front of it, and it was Mead's Hotel, at the very north end of Main Street.

Beyond it was nothing but the railroad track covered with snow, the lonely depot and the wide, open prairie. If Laura had been only a few steps nearer the others, they would all have been lost on the endless prairie north of town.

For a moment they stood by the hotel's lamplit windows. Warmth and rest were inside the hotel, but the blizzard was growing worse and they must all reach home.

Main Street would guide all of them except Ben Woodworth. No other buildings stood between the hotel and the depot where he lived. So Ben went into the hotel to stay till the blizzard was over. He could afford to do that because his father had a regular job.

Minnie and Arthur Johnson, taking the little Wilmarth boys, had only to cross Main Street to Wilmarth's grocery store and their home was beside it. The others went on down Main Street, keeping close to the buildings. They passed the saloon, they passed Royal Wilder's feed store, and then they passed Barker's grocery. The Beardsley Hotel was next and there the little Beardsley girls went in.

The journey was almost ended now. They passed Couse's Hardware store and they crossed Second Street to Fuller's Hardware. Mary Power had only to pass the drugstore now. Her father's tailor shop stood next to it.

Laura and Carrie and Teacher and Mr. Foster had to cross Main Street now. It was a wide street. But if they missed Pa's house, the haystacks and the stable were still between them and the open prairie.

They did not miss the house. One of its lighted windows made a glow that Mr. Foster saw before he ran into it. He went on around the house corner with Teacher to go by the clothesline, the haystacks, and the stable to the Garland house.

Laura and Carrie were safe at their own front door. Laura's hands fumbled at the doorknob, too stiff to turn it. Pa opened the door and helped them in.

He was wearing overcoat and cap and muffler. He had set down the lighted lantern and dropped a coil of rope. "I was just starting out after you," he said.

In the still house Laura and Carrie stood taking deep breaths. It was so quiet there where the winds did not push and pull at them. They were still blinded, but the whirling icy snow had stopped hurting their eyes.

Laura felt Ma's hands breaking away the icy muffler, and she said, "Is Carrie all right?"

"Yes, Carrie's all right," said Pa.

Ma took off Laura's hood and unbuttoned her coat and helped her pull out of its sleeves. "These wraps are driven full of ice," Ma said. They crackled when she shook them and little drifts of whiteness sifted to the floor.

"Well," Ma said, "'All's well that ends well.' You're not frostbitten. You can go to the fire and get warm."

Laura could hardly move but she stooped and with her fingers dug out the caked snow that the wind had driven in between her woolen stockings and the tops of her shoes. Then she staggered toward the stove.

"Take my place," Mary said, getting up from her rocking chair. "It's the warmest."

Laura sat stiffly down. She felt numb and stupid. She rubbed her eyes and saw a pink smear on her hand. Her eyelids were bleeding where the snow had scratched them. The sides of the coal heater glowed red-hot and she could feel the heat on her skin, but she was cold inside. The heat from the fire couldn't reach that cold.

Pa sat close to the stove holding Carrie on his knee. He had taken off her shoes to make sure that her feet were not frozen and he held her wrapped in a shawl. The shawl shivered with Carrie's shivering. "I can't get warm, Pa," she said.

"You girls are chilled through. I'll have you a hot drink in a minute," said Ma, hurrying into the kitchen.

She brought them each a steaming cup of ginger tea.

"My, that smells good!" said Mary, and Grace leaned on Laura's knee looking longingly at the cup till Laura gave her a sip and Pa said, "I don't know why there's not enough of that to go around."

"Maybe there is," said Ma, going into the kitchen again.

It was so wonderful to be there, safe at home, sheltered from the winds and the cold. Laura thought that this must be a little bit like Heaven, where the weary are at rest. She could not imagine that Heaven was better than being where she was, slowly growing warm and comfortable, sipping the hot, sweet, ginger tea, seeing Ma, and Grace, and Pa and Carrie, and Mary all enjoying their own cups of it and hearing the storm that could not touch them here.

You will enjoy reading about further adventures of the Ingalls family in *The Long Winter.* This and other books by Laura Ingalls Wilder tell the stories of her life as she was growing up.

Character Theme—Courage & Determination

Time to Think

1. Why was Laura uncomfortable in her red flannel underwear?

2. How did Laura describe the blizzard when it hit?

3. Why was the blizzard so very dangerous?

4. Why was Laura concerned about Carrie?

5. Who came to lead the students home?

6. What would have happened if Laura had not run into the side of a building?

7. How did Laura feel when she got home?

Out to Old Aunt Mary's

James Whitcomb Riley

Wasn't it pleasant, O brother mine,
In those old days of the lost sunshine
  Of youth—when the Saturday's chores were through
  And the "Sunday's wood" in the kitchen, too,
  And we went visiting, "me and you,"
      Out to Old Aunt Mary's?—

It all comes back so clear today!
Though I am as bald as you are gray,—
  Out by the barn lot and down the lane
  We patter along in the dust again,
  As light as the tips of the drops of the rain,
      Out to Old Aunt Mary's.

We cross the pastures, and through the wood,
Where the old gray snag of the poplar stood,
  Where the hammering "redheads" hopped awry,
  And the buzzard "raised" in the "clearing"-sky
  And lolled and circled, as we went by
      Out to Old Aunt Mary's.

---

snag—*a broken stump*   **lolled**—*moved in a relaxed manner*
awry—*off to one side*

And then in the dust of the road again;
And the teams we met, and the countrymen;
   And the long highway, with sunshine spread
   As thick as butter on country bread,
   Our cares behind, and our hearts ahead
      Out to Old Aunt Mary's.—

Why, I see her now in the open door
Where the little gourds grew up the sides and o'er
   The clapboard roof!—And her face—ah, me!
   Wasn't it good for a boy to see—
   And wasn't it good for a boy to be
      Out to Old Aunt Mary's?—

The jelly—the jam and the marmalade,
And the cherry and quince "preserves" she made!
   And the sweet-sour pickles of peach and pear,
   With cinnamon in 'em, and all things rare!—
   And the more we ate was the more to spare,
      Out to Old Aunt Mary's!

Ah! was there, ever, so kind a face
And gentle as hers, or such a grace
   Of welcoming, as she cut the cake
   Or the juicy pies that she joyed to make
   Just for the visiting children's sake—
      Out to Old Aunt Mary's!

The honey, too, in its amber comb
One finds only in an old farm home;
   And the coffee, fragrant and sweet, and ho!
   So hot that we gloried to drink it so,
   With spangles of tears in our eyes, you know—
      Out to Old Aunt Mary's.

And the romps we took, in our glad unrest!
Was it the lawn that we loved the best,
   With its swooping swing in the locust trees,
   Or was it the grove, with its leafy breeze,
   Or the dim haymow, with its fragrancies—
      Out to Old Aunt Mary's.

---

clapboard—*boards that overlap like shingles*
quince—*a hard applelike fruit*
spangles—*sparkling drops*

And then, in the garden—near the side
Where the beehives were and the path was wide,—
    The apple house—like a fairy cell—
    With the little square door we knew so well,
    And the wealth inside but our tongues could tell—
        Out to Old Aunt Mary's.

And the old spring-house, in the cool green gloom
Of the willow trees,—and the cooler room
    Where the swinging shelves and the crocks were kept,
    Where the cream in a golden languor slept,
    While the waters gurgled and laughed and wept—
        Out to Old Aunt Mary's.

And as many a time have you and I—
Barefoot boys in the days gone by—
    Knelt, and in tremulous ecstasies
    Dipped our lips into sweets like these,—
    Memory now is on her knees
        Out to Old Aunt Mary's.—

For, O my brother, so far away,
This is to tell you—she waits *today*
    To welcome us:—Aunt Mary fell
    Asleep this morning, whispering, "Tell
    The boys to come". . . And all is well
        Out to Old Aunt Mary's.

---

languor—*stillness*

Character Theme—Kindness
& Thankfulness

Time to Think

1. When did the boys get to go to Aunt Mary's?

2. Name some of the foods the boys enjoyed at Aunt Mary's.

3. Why is the author writing this to his brother?

THE FLAG GOES BY

Henry Holcomb Bennett

Hats off!
Along the streets there comes
A blare of bugles, a ruffle of drums,
A flash of color beneath the sky:
Hats off!
The flag is passing by!

Blue and crimson and white it shines
Over the steel-tipped, ordered lines.
Hats off!
The colors before us fly;
But more than the flag is passing by.

Sea fights and land fights, grim and great,
Fought to make and to save the State:
Weary marches and sinking ships;
Cheers of victory on dying lips;

Days of plenty and years of peace;
March of a strong land's swift increase;
Equal justice, right and law,
Stately honor and reverend awe;

Sign of a nation great and strong
To ward her people from foreign wrong:
Pride and glory and honor—all
Live in the colors to stand or fall.

Hats off!
Along the street there comes
A blare of bugles, a ruffle of drums;
And loyal hearts are beating high:
Hats off!
The flag is passing by!

Boy, Bare Your Head

Nancy Byrd Turner

Boy, bare your head when the flag goes by!
Girl, look your loyalty as it waves!
Those stars came out in a splendid sky
Over your forefathers' gallant graves:
Those stripes were fastened by heroes' hands;
Those colors flash to the farthest lands.
A bit of bunting, but how it gleams,
Fashioned of valor and woven of dreams.
The wind's in its folds, they are lifting high;
Oh, lift your hearts as the flag goes by!

Miss Louisa
and the Outlaws

Frances B. Watts

CHARACTERS

MISS LOUISA, *the schoolteacher*
THEODORE ⎫
WILLIAM ⎪
ANNABELLE ⎬ *pupils*
CLARA ⎪
REGINA ⎭
OTHER PUPILS
BENNY ⎫ *outlaws*
DEAD-EYE DAN ⎭
SHERIFF
SHERIFF'S ASSISTANT

Time: A day in October, at the turn of the 20th century.
Setting: A one-room schoolhouse. Miss Louisa's desk
　　is up right. Rows of children's desks (or tables and
　　chairs) are placed at an angle so that audience can see
　　the children. There are two vacant desks in row near-

est audience. Window is in rear wall. Door is down right; mat is in doorway. Maps and blackboard may be hung on backdrop, if desired, and books piled on desks.

AT RISE: *Miss Louisa is standing at her desk. Theodore, William, Annabelle, Clara, Regina, and other pupils sit at attention, with their hands folded.*

MISS LOUISA: For our history lesson this afternoon you all were to learn the first three stanzas of "Paul Revere's Ride." Theodore, would you come to the front of the room and recite, please? *(Theodore rises uneasily from his desk and walks slowly to front.)*

THEODORE *(Reciting haltingly):* Uh—uh—"Listen, my—children, and you—shall hear." Um—let's see—

MISS LOUISA *(Sternly):* I see that you haven't studied your lesson, Theodore. You will stay after school and learn the lines before you leave this afternoon. Do you understand?

THEODORE *(Mumbling as he slinks back to his seat):* Yes.

MISS LOUISA: Remember your manners! Yes *what*, Theodore?

THEODORE *(Straightening up and speaking with respect):* Yes, *Miss Louisa.*

MISS LOUISA: William, let's see how well you have learned the stanzas.

WILLIAM *(Walking to front, staring up at ceiling and reciting slowly):* "Listen, my children, and you shall hear." Uh—"Of the midnight ride of Paul Revere." *(Fidgets)*

MISS LOUISA: Another shirker! William, you will join Theodore after school. Do you understand?

WILLIAM *(Mumbling as he returns to his seat):* Yes.

118

MISS LOUISA: Yes *what,* William?

WILLIAM *(With respect):* Yes, *Miss Louisa.*

MISS LOUISA: Boys and girls, I realize that this poem may seem a bit dull and uninteresting. But I'm asking you to memorize it in hopes that you will recognize the courage and strength some of our forefathers possessed when they founded our great country. Do you have any idea what courage is?

PUPILS *(Together):* No, Miss Louisa.

MISS LOUISA: Courage is behaving bravely when you are most afraid. All of us, at some time, have been afraid. Those who discipline themselves and control fear in times of stress are exhibiting courage. Is that clear?

PUPILS *(Together):* Yes, Miss Louisa.

WILLIAM *(Whispering to Theodore):* I'll bet Miss Louisa has never been afraid in her life! All she ever does is scare *us* to death!

THEODORE *(Aside):* You said it. What does she know about fear? All she has in her veins is ice water!

MISS LOUISA: Annabelle, will you recite the lines for us?

ANNABELLE: Yes, Miss Louisa. *(She goes confidently to front and recites)*

> Listen, my children, and you shall hear
> Of the midnight ride of Paul Revere. . . .

(She recites first two verses. Benny and Dead-Eye Dan suddenly enter down right. They are dressed as outlaws and draw their guns.)

BENNY: Stay where you are!

THEODORE *(Fearfully):* Outlaws! It's Benny, the Kid, and Dead-Eye Dan! The ones who robbed Dodge City Bank last week!

WILLIAM: You're right! It is! Their pictures are up in the Post Office. Wanted, dead or alive! A hundred dollars reward! *(Pupils scream with terror. Some run to back of the room. Miss Louisa raps on desk with a ruler.)*

MISS LOUISA *(Speaking sternly):* Back to your seats, everyone! How often have I told you never to leave your seats without permission! *(Timidly, but obediently, pupils return to seats.)*

DAN: Nobody's going to get hurt, kiddies, as long as you set there quiet.

MISS LOUISA *(With great dignity):* Watch your grammar in front of my pupils, sir. The proper expression is—*sit there quietly*—not *set there quiet.*

DAN *(Baffled):* Huh? Oh. *(Corrects himself)* As long as you *sit there quietly.*

BENNY: Just in case somebody tipped off the Sheriff that we're in town, my pal Dan and me are going to hide out here till the two-thirty freight train comes through. Then we'll make our getaway. So don't nobody get any bright ideas like yelling out the window or running for help, see? *(Flourishes gun while pupils cower in fear.)*

DAN *(Nodding at two vacant desks):* Let's take a load off our feet, Benny. May as well be comfortable till train time.

MISS LOUISA *(Firmly):* Just a moment, Daniel! I believe that is your name. You and Benjamin will kindly wipe your feet on this mat before you sit down. *(Points to mat in doorway)*

BENNY *(In confusion):* Say, what is this? Dan and me got guns. We don't have to take orders from you.

MISS LOUISA: It's Dan and *I have* guns, sir. And as long as you and Benjamin take refuge here, I shall insist that you obey the laws and rules of our schoolhouse. Kindly wipe your feet, gentlemen! *(She stares at them.)*

DAN *(Grudgingly):* All right. All right. We'll wipe our feet.

MISS LOUISA: Mind your manners, sir. When I speak to you, you are to answer, "Yes, Miss Louisa." Do you understand?

BENNY AND DAN *(Meekly):* Yes, Miss Louisa. *(They wipe their feet, then tiptoe to vacant desks. They keep guns in hand.)*

BENNY *(Aside to Dan; puzzled):* I don't know why we let this schoolteacher lead us around by the nose. By all rights we ought to tie her up in the closet.

MISS LOUISA *(Briskly):* Boys and girls, we shall continue our history lesson tomorrow. It is now time for music. Let's have a song—a jolly one. How about "Old MacDonald Had a Farm"?

REGINA *(Timidly):* We can't sing, Miss Louisa. We're too scared! *(Lays head on desk and sobs)*

MISS LOUISA: Afraid, Regina? Of what is there to be afraid? As far as we are concerned, we simply have two extra pupils in our room. We will follow our usual schedule. *(Coolly takes pitch pipe from her pocket and sounds the key. Class begins to sing "Old MacDonald." Benny and Dan do not sing. Miss Louisa interrupts song by rapping with ruler. Speaks to outlaws)* Benjamin and Daniel, why aren't you singing?

DAN *(Bewildered):* Huh? Why should we sing?

CLARA *(Earnestly):* When we have music in this school, everybody sings.

ANNABELLE *(Nodding):* And that means *everybody.* It's a school rule.

MISS LOUISA *(To Clara and Annabelle):* Clara and Annabelle, this is not your affair. *(To outlaws, firmly)* When we start to sing again, you will sing. Do you understand?

BENNY *(Mumbling):* Yes.

MISS LOUISA: Yes, *what,* Benjamin?

BENNY: Yes, Miss Louisa. *(Miss Louisa blows her pipe again and waves her arms as she leads the song. Pupils sing; Benny and Dan sing, also. All begin to smile and appear cheerful as they sing. At end of song, Miss Louisa crosses to window, with a worried frown. Benny hops up, draws gun.)* Stay away from that window, ma'am. We're not giving you the chance to signal for help.

DAN *(Drawing gun):* You may be a schoolmarm, but you can't outsmart us. Nobody has ever outsmarted Benny, the Kid, and Dead-Eye Dan. *(Miss Louisa remains at window, speaks matter-of-factly.)*

MISS LOUISA: It looks a bit like rain. William, will you and Theodore please go out and bring in the flag? *(William and Theodore rise to obey.)*

BENNY *(To Miss Louisa):* Do you think we're stupid? Why, the minute those kids leave this room they'll run for the Sheriff.

WILLIAM *(Nervously):* Don't make us go, Miss Louisa! It really doesn't look like rain.

MISS LOUISA: There are cumulus clouds forming in the west. It is October; showers begin suddenly in the fall. *(To outlaws)* It is a rule of our school that we never allow the American flag to become wet. One of you

122

may accompany the boys, if you wish. But our flag must not be rained upon! Do you hear?

BENNY *(Exasperated):* Oh, all right, then.

MISS LOUISA *(Sternly):* What did you say?

BENNY *(Meekly):* Yes, Miss Louisa. *(He heads toward door and motions to William and Theodore to precede him. They exit. Dan keeps his gun drawn.)*

MISS LOUISA: Now, boys and girls, we will have a spelling bee. Regina and Clara may be captains. You may start choosing teams, girls.

REGINA: I choose Annabelle.

CLARA: I choose Margaret. *(They continue choosing sides, calling out various children's names. The teams line up on opposite sides of stage and face audience. Benny, Theodore, and William, who carries flag, appear at doorway, and wipe feet carefully before entering room. William hands flag to Miss Louisa, who folds it and puts it on her desk.)*

REGINA *(Continuing with choosing):* I choose Theodore for my team. *(Theodore takes his place.)*

CLARA: I choose William. *(William takes his place.)*

REGINA: I choose Daniel. *(Dan takes his place, and tucks gun in holster.)*

CLARA: I choose Benjamin.

BENNY: Say, what is this? What's going on?

DAN *(With enthusiasm):* A spelling bee, pal. Ain't you never been in a spelling bee before?

MISS LOUISA: *Haven't you ever,* Daniel. Watch that grammar!

DAN *(Correcting himself):* Haven't you ever been in a spelling bee before?

BENNY: No, and I'm not going to now. Besides, it'll be train time soon. We have to stay on the alert.

MISS LOUISA *(Pausing, then nodding sympathetically):* Very well, Benjamin. I will excuse you from participating in the spelling bee. Naturally, it would be most embarrassing for you to be spelled down by a group of young children.

BENNY *(Blustering):* Who's scared of being spelled down? Look, maybe I haven't had much schooling, but I'm not so dumb that a bunch of little kids can lick me at spelling.

MISS LOUISA: I admire your spirit, Benjamin. You won't mind joining Clara's team, then.

BENNY: Oh, all right.

MISS LOUISA *(Severely):* What's that, Benjamin?

BENNY: Yes, Miss Louisa. *(He takes his place at the end of Clara's line and puts gun in holster. Miss Louisa stands center stage, holding spelling book.)*

MISS LOUISA: Clara, we'll begin with you. Spell "democracy."

CLARA *(Spelling confidently):* D-e-m-o-c-r-a-c-y.

MISS LOUISA: That's correct, Clara. *(She continues to call out words for pupils to spell, in turn. When a word is spelled correctly, Dan and Benny join pupils in cheering and applauding. Miss Louisa addresses Benny.)* Now, Benjamin, I would like you to spell the word, "thief."

BENNY *(Raising eyes to ceiling):* Lemme see. Thief. T—h. *(Hesitates)* T-H-E-I-F.

MISS LOUISA: That is wrong, Benjamin. The correct spelling is t-h-i-e-f. You may take your seat.

124

WILLIAM *(Aside):* . . . . He *is* a thief, and he can't even spell it!

BENNY *(Stomping sulkily to his desk):* Aw, so what if I'm not a good speller. I still make a good living. *(Sound of a train whistle is heard. It gradually increases in volume.)*

DAN *(Rushing to window):* Yeow! There goes the two-thirty freight train!

BENNY *(Running over to window, stamping angrily):* I told you it was time to get out of here! But you had to let that crazy schoolteacher talk us into a spelling bee!

DAN: All right. All right. At least *I* didn't miss my spelling word. *(Sheriff and Assistant enter suddenly.)*

SHERIFF *(Drawing gun):* Hands up! *(Outlaws raise hands. Sheriff and Assistant steer them toward the door.)*

THEODORE: Sheriff, how did you know the outlaws were here?

SHERIFF: I didn't know, son. But I knew something was wrong when I happened to look out of my office window and saw that the school flagpole was bare. Why, you know as well as I do that unless it's raining, Miss Louisa never lowers the flag until sundown. It's a rule of the school. Remember, Miss Louisa was my teacher, too.

MISS LOUISA *(To Sheriff):* I was hoping you'd notice that the flag was down, and would remember that rule, Rodney. Apparently my pupils remember *some* things that I teach them.

ANNABELLE: Miss Louisa was just like Paul Revere's friend. She used a signal to tell about the enemy!

MISS LOUISA: That's right, Annabelle. *(To outlaws)* And if you gentlemen were the slightest bit educated about the ways of the weather, you would have known that cumulus clouds in the west rarely mean immediate rain.

BENNY *(To Dan):* I had a hunch that we should have tied that teacher up in the closet the minute we came in!

DAN: Could *you* have tied her up?

BENNY *(Scratching his head in bewilderment):* No, I guess I couldn't have at that. There's something about Miss Louisa. You just can't imagine tying her up in a closet. *(Pauses)* She doesn't scare easy, and before you know it, you're half-scared of *her.*

MISS LOUISA: The proper grammar, Benjamin, is—she doesn't scare easily.

BENNY: Yes, Miss Louisa.

SHERIFF: We'll take these scoundrels down to jail where they belong. You'll receive the hundred dollars' reward in a few days, Miss Louisa.

Miss Louisa: Thank you, Rodney. I believe it will be just enough money to take the children on an outing to the Dodge City music festival.

Pupils *(Elated; ad lib):* The Dodge City music festival! Hooray! *(Etc.)*

Miss Louisa: Now, children, I believe that I will dismiss you for the rest of the afternoon.

Pupils: Hooray! Hooray for Miss Louisa! *(They exit noisily. Miss Louisa sits limply at her desk, and holds head in hands. After a moment, William and Theodore appear at doorway, re-enter tentatively. Miss Louisa looks up and sees them.)* Did you boys forget something?

Theodore: You asked us to stay and learn the first three stanzas of "Paul Revere's Ride," Miss Louisa.

Miss Louisa: Oh, so I did. Well, I will excuse you just this once. You see, I'm feeling a bit shaky. *(Rubs forehead)*

William *(Thoughtfully)*: Miss Louisa, you were afraid when the outlaws were here, weren't you?

Miss Louisa: Oh, yes. Very much afraid. I did everything in my power to delay them, so that they might miss the train and be captured. Yet, I longed for them to leave before they decided to use those wicked guns on some of us.

Theodore: You didn't act scared. Not one bit!

William *(Stoutly):* Naturally, she didn't! She behaved bravely when she was most afraid. That's *courage.* Remember?

Miss Louisa *(smiling):* Perhaps I taught you something today after all. *(She takes flag from desk and hands it to William.)* Before you leave, boys, please hoist the flag again. It's several hours yet until sundown. We must abide by the rules of the school, you know.

WILLIAM *(With admiration):* Yes, Miss Louisa.

THEODORE *(With a quick bow of respect):* Yes, indeed. Goodbye, Miss Louisa. *(Boys exit, as curtain falls.)*

THE END

Character Theme—Courage & Resourcefulness

God's Word Says   *2 Chronicles 19:11*

Deal courageously, and the Lord shall be with the good.

Time to Think

1. Why did Miss Louisa want the students to memorize "Paul Revere's Ride"?

2. How did Miss Louisa define courage?

3. How did Miss Louisa show courage when the outlaws came to the schoolhouse?

4. What did Miss Louisa do to outsmart the outlaws?

5. What kind of teacher was Miss Louisa?

The Children's Song

Rudyard Kipling

Land of our Birth, we pledge to thee
Our love and toil in the years to be;
When we are grown and take our place
As men and women with our race.

Father in Heaven who lovest all,
Oh, help Thy children when they call;
That they may build from age to age
An undefiled heritage.

Teach us to bear the yoke in youth,
With steadfastness and careful truth;
That, in our time, Thy Grace may give
The Truth whereby the Nations live.

Teach us to rule ourselves alway,
Controlled and cleanly night and day;
That we may bring, if need arise,
No maimed or worthless sacrifice.

Teach us to look in all our ends,
On Thee for judge, and not our friends;
That we, with Thee, may walk uncowed
By fear or favor of the crowd.

Teach us the Strength that cannot seek,
By deed or thought, to hurt the weak;
That, under Thee, we may possess
Man's strength to comfort man's distress.

Teach us Delight in simple things,
And Mirth that has no bitter springs;
Forgiveness free of evil done,
And Love to all men 'neath the sun!

Land of our Birth, our faith, our pride,
For whose dear sake our fathers died;
O Motherland, we pledge to thee
Head, heart, and hand through the years to be!

---

maimed—*made imperfect*
uncowed—*not frightened by threats*
mirth—*happiness characterized by laughter*

Nothing turns out right
unless someone makes it his job
to see that it does.

Beneath the Saddle

Russell Gordon Carter

Nathan Cathcart sat upright in bed, his heart pounding. In his ears still rang the pistol shot that had awakened him, and from the frozen road at the base of the hill came the clatter of hoof beats. He was about to hurry to the window when a heavy object struck the front door, causing the whole house to tremble.

"Open in the King's name!" came a harsh voice. And another added, "Aye, and be quick!"

Nathan felt his throat tighten. He thought of his mother and longed for her comforting presence, for he was all alone in the little farmhouse. These men at the door were British soldiers; there could be little doubt of that!

With teeth chattering, the boy got hastily into his clothes and made his way down the steep narrow stairway. As he reached the door, it jarred under the powerful blows that threatened to splinter it.

"Who is there?" he called in a shaking voice.

"You will soon find out if you keep us waiting longer!"

Nathan drew aside the heavy oak bar and lifted the latch, and with a rush of cold air the door swung inward. In front of him stood two British soldiers in scarlet uniforms. Beyond them he had a glimpse of others, on their way up the hill, leading their horses.

"Whose house is this?" demanded one of the men in the doorway. As he spoke, the two of them strode inside.

"I—I live here with my mother," Nathan replied. "Tonight I'm alone, because she had to go to Norfolk to nurse my aunt, who is ill."

"Well, young rebel," the soldier ordered, "go fetch candles, for we mean to have a look about. Mind you lose no time!"

Nathan hesitated, then went into the living room, where squares of moonlight lay upon the wide floor. Why did these men wish to search the house? What could they expect to find?

In a few minutes he was back in the hallway with two lighted candles in brass candlesticks. By that time the rest of the party had reached the house. They strode noisily inside and then closed the door.

"You wait right here, young puppy," one of them said to Nathan.

"But—but what is it you are seeking?" the boy asked.

"Never you mind that," was the reply.

Shivering with cold and excitement, Nathan stood silent beside the door. There were now almost a dozen soldiers in the house, some of them upstairs, some on the lower floor. The candles, which they carried from room to room, sent queer shadows dancing wildly about on walls and floor and ceiling. From snatches of conversation, Nathan understood that they were searching for someone, but he could not find out who it might be.

At last those on the second floor came clumping down the stairs. "We are wasting our time here!" one of them shouted. Then the whole party went outside. Standing in the doorway, Nathan saw them mount their horses and ride down the hillside toward the road.

Closing the door, he went upstairs. There he found the bedrooms in great disorder. On the floor of his own room a candle was burning dangerously close to the bed covering. He carried it downstairs and placed it upon the high mantlepiece above the fireplace, where the soldiers had left the second one. Despite the cold that filled the room, he stood for some time motionless before the hearth, his head bent, his forehead wrinkled. Who was it the British soldiers were seeking? He remembered the pistol that had awakened him. What did it all mean?

Outside the wind was rising. He heard the mournful sound of it in the chimney and among the pines that sheltered the house on the northwest. Now and then a beam would crack with the cold. The boy hunched his shoulders and thought of his bed with its warm blankets.

Stepping forward, he snuffed out the candles. He was on his way toward the stairs when a gentle knock at the door caused him to stiffen and catch his breath. His first thought was that the soldiers had returned. "But no redcoat would knock like that!" he thought to himself. He went close to the door. "Who is there?" he asked.

"A friend," came the reply in a low voice.

Nathan hesitated. "Who are you?" he demanded.

"A friend," the voice repeated.

Nathan swung the door open and then uttered a little cry of surprise. There in the moonlight stood a man in the uniform of the American army, a bloodstained kerchief round his head. In a flash the boy understood. This was the man for whom the British were searching!

"Thank ye, lad," said the stranger as he entered the house. "The night is cold—"

"And they've wounded you!"

"Aye, that is true, but 'tis not a bad wound." The man laughed bitterly. "So they thought to find me in the house, eh? Little they knew that I was watching while they came up the hill! You are alone here, lad?"

"Yes," said Nathan. "My mother is at Norfolk for a day or two."

In the living room the stranger dropped wearily upon a bench in front of the hearth and covered his face with his hands. "A sorry mess I have made of things!" he muttered.

Nathan listened uneasily. "What has happened, sir?" he said. "I—I would like to be of help, if there is anything that I can do!"

The man lifted his head. "Lad," he said, "I have made a sorry mess of an important errand. My name is Dawson, and I was carrying important papers from General Washington, at White Plains. The British laid an ambush for me. I tried to escape them by desperate riding, but they fired, and a pistol ball grazed the side of my head, causing me to lose control of my horse. The creature raced up the road and then bolted into the woods, where a branch swept me to the ground. They found my horse, but they were unable to find me!"

"Oh," exclaimed Nathan, "then 'tis not so bad after all!"

"Not so bad?" repeated the messenger. "In truth, affairs could hardly be worse!"

Nathan looked at him wonderingly.

"The papers I carried were on the horse," Dawson added bitterly. "I had thrust the packet 'twixt saddle and blanket, thinking it would be safe, and now the British have my horse! They will soon discover the packet, if they have not already come upon it, and then—" He flung out his hands in despair. "Ah, if only—"

He suddenly checked himself and rose to his feet. From the direction of the road came the ring and clatter of hoof beats and the sound of excited voices. The British soldiers were returning!

"Come!" cried Nathan, seizing the man's arm. "You must hide!"

"Aye, but where?" Dawson glanced wildly about.

Nathan strode to the great fireplace and stepped inside. With shoulder against the wooden wall at one end, he pressed until it yielded, revealing an opening perhaps a foot wide. "Squeeze in there!" he ordered. "Then push the wall back into place. My grandfather once hid there from the Indians. You will be safe if you make no sound. Quick!" He pushed the man forward.

Only when the panel had closed behind the stranger was Nathan able to control his trembling hands. Running to the window, he beheld the whole troop riding at a fast pace up the hillside. What should he do? Suddenly he ran to the door, slid back the bar which had held it fast, and then went swiftly up the stairway to his room. He flung himself into his cold bed.

A few seconds later he heard the soldiers in the hall, then in the lower rooms. He lay with thumping heart while the stairs resounded under the tread of heavy boots. Now the redcoats were on the second floor. Now they were in his room! One of them held up a candle, revealing the boy sitting up, wide-eyed, in bed, the blankets about his shoulders.

"Where is the rebel horseman? Where is he hiding?"

Nathan swallowed hard and remained silent.

"Speak up, young whelp!"

Before the boy could answer, a soldier caught hold of him and flung him onto the floor. Then they began to prod the mattress with the points of their swords.

Bruised and shaken, Nathan rose and made his way downstairs, intending to flee to the nearby woods. As he stepped from the doorway, he almost ran into a soldier who was holding the bridles of half a dozen horses.

"Wait a bit, lad!" the man exclaimed, and his voice sounded kind. "Wait a bit, I say. We mean ye no harm, and that is the truth!"

Nathan hesitated.

"'Tis a cold night!" said the soldier, blowing on his hands. "The horses feel it, too!"

Steam from their nostrils rose white and sparkling in the moonlight. The frozen earth rang under their restlessly stamping feet.

"They are fine-looking horses, sir," Nathan remarked with an effort.

"Aye, fine animals indeed!"

The boy was studying them carefully. Which was the dispatch rider's horse? He singled out a sleek black mare that looked more tired than the others. And then he noticed that her saddle was different from the other saddles!

In a friendly, careless manner, he walked over to her and patted her nose. At that moment one of the soldiers stepped to the doorway and began to talk to the man who held the bridles. Nathan heard no word of what they were saying, for his fingers were upon the mare's blanket, creeping upward under the saddle, while the terrific beating of his heart seemed to jar his whole body! At last his fingers touched something . . . something. . . . Just then one of the British horses nipped at the black mare, and she backed away, almost knocking the boy over.

"Steady, there!" yelled the redcoat, and then he continued his talk with the man in the doorway.

As Nathan thrust his fingers under the saddle again, he heard the soldiers coming down the stairs. Evidently the search was ended, and they were about to ride off! Again his hand was touching something beneath the saddle. With thumb and forefinger upon a corner of the object, he drew it slowly downward. The moonlight flashed for an instant on an oblong white packet as he jerked it forth and thrust it beneath his shirt.

Nathan was nowhere in sight when the British rode off. He had run to the shelter of a brush heap at the north of the house, ready to retreat further into the woods if the soldiers should decide to hunt for him. But they were not interested in a mere boy. They had searched the house twice and were satisfied that the rebel horseman was not within.

The British had been gone at least a quarter of an hour when Nathan entered the living room and thrust his shoulder against the panel at the end of the fireplace. Dawson stepped forth, blinking in the candlelight. "Eh, what—what—?"

"I took it from beneath the saddle," said Nathan.

"You—you—what?" With a hoarse cry the man seized the packet and examined it. Then his legs wavered under him, and he sat down hard upon the bench. "Lad!" he muttered. "You—you tricked them!" Suddenly he sprang to his feet and threw his arms about Nathan's shoulders. "You've done me a service! Aye, you've done your country a service! I'll never forget it as long as I live! Tell me your name, lad!"

"Nathan Cathcart, sir."

"Cathcart, eh? I'll not be likely to forget that name! I had a friend, Jack Cathcart, who fell at Bunker Hill."

"He was my father," Nathan said in a low voice. For several seconds the man and boy stood facing each other in silence. . .

"Well, lad," the soldier said at last, "I must be off. The Blue Fox Tavern lies but a few miles up the road, and there I can get another horse. Your hand, Nathan, and I promise you that General Washington shall hear of what has happened this night!"

Nathan watched him as he made his way down the slope in the moonlight. Then the boy climbed the stairs once more to his room, this time to undisturbed sleep!

Character Theme—Initiative & Courage

Time to Think

1. What suddenly woke Nathan during the middle of the night?

2. During which war did this story take place?

3. Why were the Redcoats looking for Dawson?

4. What clues told Nathan he had found the messenger's horse?

5. How had Nathan done his country a service?

Johnny Appleseed

1775–1847

Stephen Vincent Benét

Of Jonathan Chapman
Two things are known,
That he loved apples,
That he walked alone.

At seventy-odd
He was gnarled as could be,
But ruddy and sound
As a good apple tree.

For fifty years over
Of harvest and dew,
He planted his apples
Where no apples grew.

The winds of the prairie
Might blow through his rags,
But he carried his seeds
In the best deerskin bags.

From old Ashtabula
To frontier Fort Wayne,
He planted and pruned
And he planted again.

He had not a hat
To encumber his head.
He wore a tin pan
On his white hair instead.

---

gnarled—*rough and twisted from age*   **encumber**—*add a burden to*
ruddy—*having a healthy color*
Ashtabula (ăsh′tə·bōō′lə)—*a city in Ohio on Lake Erie*

140

He nested with owl,
And with bear cub and possum,
And knew all his orchards
Root, tendril and blossom.

A fine old man,
As ripe as a pippin,
His heart still light,
And his step still skipping.

The stalking Indian,
The beast in its lair
Did no hurt
While he was there.

For they could tell,
As wild things can,
That Jonathan Chapman
Was God's own man.

Why did he do it?
We do not know.
He wished that apples
Might root and grow.

He has no statue.
He has no tomb.
He has his apple trees
Still in bloom.

Consider, consider,
Think well upon
The marvelous story
Of Appleseed John.

pippin—*an apple*
lair—*the home of a wild animal*

141

In the summer of 1893,
Katherine Lee Bates took a trip
to the top of Pike's Peak in Colorado.
The view inspired her to write
"America the Beautiful."
This patriotic poem was set to music
in 1910 by Samuel Augustus Ward.

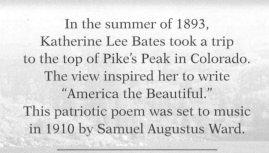

AMERICA THE BEAUTIFUL

Katherine Lee Bates

O beautiful for spacious skies,
For amber waves of grain,
For purple mountain majesties
Above the fruited plain!
America!
America!
God shed His grace on thee,
And crown thy good with brotherhood
From sea to shining sea.

Hasty Pudding

Cornelia Meigs

If it had not been for the thought of the hasty pudding, the little Stowe house would have been somewhat doleful that spring morning. As it was, there was hurry and bustle everywhere, with everyone telling everyone else what to do. The cold spring wind was banging the shutters, and every now and then a spurt of chilly rain would sweep across the gray hillside and throw itself against the windows. But no one—at least none of the children—noticed it at all. Ten-year-old Betty, who was to have charge of the house while her mother was away, was too full of questions about this and that to think about anything that might be going on outside. In fact, she was so busy asking questions that she did not always attend to the answers. Certainly she did not see that her mother's

---

doleful—*sad, mournful*

face looked troubled and that her father was whistling the tune that one only heard when he was a little anxious.

The small log house where the Stowe family lived was on the great far-spread hillside farm which their father had cut out of the Vermont woods for them. It had only one drawback, that of being very far from any town or other house. This was the time when the State of Vermont, with its tall mountains and narrow, green valleys, had but few people in it. Those who had been bold enough to clear the ground of forest and settle down to live there were very comfortable and happy, but they were not many. Twice a year it was necessary for Mr. and Mrs. Stowe to take the long journey to buy needed things at the nearest town, thirty miles away and on the other side of the mountain. They would be gone two days, but they would stop on the way and ask Great-Uncle Richard and Great-Aunt Clara, who lived fifteen miles down the valley, to come up and stay with the three children. But these two could not arrive so very soon, so that the three Stowes must spend the whole day alone. It was what every family, and every group of children, had to do in those early days of the settling of Vermont.

Therefore, it was Betty, with her straight shoulders, her quick feet, and her bright black eyes, who was to be in command while they were by themselves. Tom, who was nine, was perfectly able to carry the grain and water to the cows and feed the pigs. Martha was seven; she was to scatter corn for the chickens and help with the dishwashing. But it was Betty who must see that everything went properly, that the house was tidy, the meals cooked, and, if Uncle Richard and Aunt Clara should chance to be late, she must even see that everyone went to bed early, that the fire was covered, and the door barred.

On the evening before, Betty was sitting up in bed in her little room under the roof, wrapped up in a patchwork quilt, while she talked to her mother. "I must remember all those things," she said, "but I am not very good at remembering."

"No," her mother agreed, "you forget things easily, especially when you are in a hurry. But this kind of thing will help you to learn to remember. You *have* to remember when a whole family is depending on you. That is how I learned not to forget things."

Betty had a sudden feeling that was not quite terror, but something very much like it. Things were so safe and comfortable when her mother was there, and so different when she was gone. But she knew perfectly well that children had to stay alone when their parents went away to have the grain ground and to buy sugar and coffee and salt, and such things as they could not get along without. Younger ones than she had managed, for they had to do it. Wildcats would call in the thickets on the mountainside; but everyone knew that wildcats never did harm to people, only to chickens and perhaps baby pigs. And there were other things—but she would not allow herself to think of them. She turned her mind stoutly to something else.

"Mother," she said, "I'm going to make them hasty pudding. They all like it so much, Tom particularly. You showed me once, and I know I can do it again. They will really understand that I can cook, when they see it come out of the pot all hot and smoking."

---

stoutly—*bravely, determinedly*

145

She let her mother tuck her in and listened to her footsteps as Mrs. Stowe went down to her own room below.

Betty went to sleep thinking of how fine it would be, that hot, spicy smell of the finished pudding, and what respect the other two children would have for her when she drew it out of the brick oven.

The log cottage was stout and warm, even though it was so small. There were two rooms below, the big kitchen where they all worked and ate and played, and the little bedroom behind it, where their father and mother, and Martha, the littlest girl, slept. Up under the roof were two tiny rooms for Tom and Betty, with the warm, stone chimney going up through both of them. There were no real stairs, only a broad, stout ladder, by which one climbed up from below. The children had known nothing else. They ran up and down like squirrels, thinking always that their house was the most beautiful and the most convenient one in the world. Betty, just before she went to sleep, could always see a picture of it behind her eyelids; how it looked to the stars, perhaps, or to the cold white moon coming up behind the mountains. It would be so small and square and tight, and its column of smoke would be going up so steadily and bravely in all that empty night of big white mountains and bright moon staring down.

In the morning, as has been said, her heart might have failed a little if she had not thought about the hasty pudding. Her mother showed her where everything was that she would need. Then, in a hail of good-byes and parting messages, Mr. and Mrs. Stowe climbed into the low wagon, clucked to the big gray horses, and were off.

146

"Be sure to keep the fire going. Be sure to bar the door well when it begins to get dark." Those were their mother's last words. It was so early that the clear, bright dawn was just lighting the stretch of sky above the hills. All the mountaintops were wrapped in a blanket of snow, but the long slopes were bare and dark, with here and there a glint of something sparkling, which was a little lake or an open stretch of some quickly running mountain stream. The wagon would be in sight for an hour, moving down the rough track which they called a road, and which wound away through the valley. Then presently, toward the end of the day, they would see a fat white horse coming slowly up and up the long way, a cart would stop at the door and Great-Aunt Clara would get down and say, "Well, children," just as she always did, and Uncle Richard would climb down after her, carrying the long rifle that always went with him, for who knew when one might meet a deer!

Betty turned away, finally, for nothing would be done in the house if they watched too long. She swept, she built up the fire, she skimmed the milk and kneaded down the bread. It takes a great many steps and a great deal of work to make even a little log house spotless and comfortable and warm. She had not known how often one had to put wood in the fireplace when one did it all alone. Tom was doing his full share in the barn, throwing down hay, putting fresh straw in stalls, bringing water, and filling up mangers with corn. He and Betty exchanged shouts through the window and across the narrow yard, as they worked, each at his own task.

They lingered long over their dinner, because they had worked so hard all morning and because there was such an endless stream of jokes and stories to tell. Perhaps it was the fact that they must wash the dishes alone that made them slow about getting up and setting about another task. The rain had begun to come down steadily and streamed down the windows. It was only an April storm, they felt sure, but it might delay Uncle Richard and Aunt Clara. Tom was tired from his busy morning and was willing indeed to sit on his stool beside the fire, even after Betty had asked him twice to go out and draw some water.

"There's no hurry about anything," he answered. "Why should I go out to the well in all this rain? I'll get some presently."

Betty, also, did not mind very much sitting in her mother's chair and looking, just looking, into the book which their mother had been reading to them last night. Little Martha, thoroughly tired out, curled up in the window seat; Tom dropped into his father's chair and was nodding, then finally went to sleep. Betty read on; she did not notice that the rain had stopped, that the sun shone briefly and then went under a cloud again. At last she jumped up and looked at the clock. The best part of the afternoon was gone. She must begin getting supper ready, build up the fire, put the kettle on to boil, and run out to milk the cow. Tom was only fairly good at milking, so their father said that Betty must do it.

She hurried to the barn with the empty pail in her hand; she was almost running when she came back with it full and foaming. The fire was bright on the hearth, Martha had been putting on extra logs. Now was the time for the hasty pudding. It was strange that their aunt and uncle had not come yet; but the heavy rain must have delayed them, and after all Betty could do very well at getting supper alone. Aunt Clara might scold a little when she found that Betty had let the work get behind. It was nearly suppertime, and she had not yet begun the pudding. They were going to have hasty pudding for supper, Betty vowed, if she had to toil until midnight.

Hasty pudding is not a real pudding at all, but porridge made of milk and flour, which if stirred smooth and combined with the proper flavors, can be made most delicious. Betty began to weigh and measure, but she was in such a hurry that she lost count of the cups of flour and had to measure and count again. At last she had the pudding mixed and set over the fire in the iron pot. It must cook slowly and be stirred again and again, and meanwhile she had a hundred things to do. Martha looked tired and hungry. She sat down with a sigh and uttered the first lamentation of the day.

"I wish Mother were here."

Tom had come in from the barn. He had been working hard and was all ready to grumble. "Yes, if Mother was here we wouldn't have to wait like this for supper."

"I'm doing the best I can," returned Betty. She remembered just in time that she was in charge of the house and so managed to keep her voice from sounding snappish. "You'll see, supper will be ready before you know it."

She was feeling tired, too, and flurried at last, and not very sure of herself. She took off the cover of the pot and a delicious, comforting puff of fragrant steam came out. At least all was well with the pudding. The whiff of hot goodness made the others feel a little more cheerful. They

could not help
much, but they
kept out of the
way as Betty
rushed from the
fireplace to the
table and back
again. "In a
few minutes
now," she kept
announcing,
and at last gave
the welcome news,
"There, supper
is ready." It was
almost dark.

They pulled up their seats to the circle of firelight,
for the evening was cold, as spring evenings are. The
bacon was good, so were the potatoes, browned before
the blaze. "But wait, just you wait," Betty kept telling
them.

Now came the great moment. She went to the
fireplace, took off the cover of the pot, and gave a final
stir with the big spoon. The pudding was just the right
thickness; here again was the marvelous smell pouring
out. She had just lifted the pot, very carefully, off the
fire, when she stopped suddenly. There was sound on the
doorstep outside, an uncertain shuffling noise. Could it
be Aunt Clara—could it be? It was in that second that
she knew she had forgotten her mother's instruction,
"Don't forget to bar the door as soon as it is dark."

She had forgotten. The door was shut, but the least touch on the wooden latch would open it. And the noise outside, what was it? Certainly not Uncle Richard or Aunt Clara.

She shot a glance of terror across the table. Tom had half risen from his stool; he, too, knew that this was an unusual sound. Martha alone was quite unconscious that anything was wrong. She took up her spoon and cried out in delight at the sight and the smell of the hasty pudding. But Betty stood, frozen, with the pot in her hand; for the wooden peg of the latch moved and the door swung open. The firelight showed two little glittering eyes, a smooth furry back; it showed, in short, that the thing which stood on the threshold was a round, plump, black bear.

Bears are not very terrible to see; they are not larger than big dogs, and their little pointed faces have always, somehow, a comic look. When one sees a bear one is not apt, at once, to feel frightened. But there is something about the idea of a wild animal from the woods coming into your house, a hungry animal which will take whatever it wants without asking, that is not soothing or comforting. Betty put down the pot with the pudding as carefully as she had taken it up, for even at this moment she could not drop anything that had seemed so precious. Then she cried out, "Run, Martha, run, Tom. Up the ladder. Let the bear have what he wants. Then he won't bother us."

Up they went, on feet that never stumbled, Betty helping Martha for fear she might fall. The ladder was steep, but they were so used to climbing it that they reached the top without a misstep, in spite of their breakneck haste. Once there, they sat down in a row, with their feet dangling over the beam which ran all across the house. Through Betty's mind there went over and over again the thought, "If I had remembered to fasten the door, if I had only remembered to fasten the door as Mother said. I was in such a hurry over the pudding that I forgot it." Even while she was so thinking, a draught of air, blowing through the house, caught the door and banged it to. The peg of the latch slipped as it often did when the door was slammed and it was fastened.

The bear stood staring at the fire for a minute, afraid of it, but enjoying its warmth. He came to the table, rose easily on his hind feet, and slipped the bacon off every plate. It was plain that he was pleased, he licked his jaws and looked about for more. He moved easily and quickly and neatly, like a dog which has been trained to stand on his hind legs. Suddenly he seemed to feel displeased over finding no more bacon, for he shouldered against the table and upset it. There was a great crash of broken china and of pewter spoons, while he snuffed and smelled among the wreckage, licking up what suited him. Still he did not seem satisfied and, as he turned about, a delicious fragrance seemed to come to his nostrils, the scent of the hasty pudding.

He swung round, came close to the hearth, and plunged his nose into the covered pot. The porridge was still hot, hot enough to burn his unaccustomed tongue and lips. He backed away, sat down on his haunches, and put both paws to his nose. He sat there, rolling from side to side, not in much pain probably, but in great anger and surprise.

The ridiculous sight was too much for Martha, and she laughed aloud. He lifted his head, listening, then turned about and, for the first time, saw the children. For a full minute they stared at each other. Then he got on all fours, came shambling across the room, and began to climb the ladder.

The three had not been greatly frightened, for they had seen bears at a distance before and had been told that they did no harm unless someone struck or hurt them. But to have a bear come climbing up to the perch upon which they sat, to the little loft where there was no room to move about, that was disturbing, very disturbing indeed. But up he came, rung by rung, for bears can climb as easily and neatly as they can do many other things. Betty, who sat nearest, knew that she must think of something quickly, now, before he came a step nearer.

The sides of the ladder, where they rested against the beam, were held between big spikes or nails, two on each side, so that the ladder was steady, but could be moved if necessary. "Tom, Tom," Betty ordered in a whisper, so that she would not excite the bear, "take hold of the other side of the ladder and pull, pull hard, so that we can push it out from the beam."

It took a strong jerk from both the children to wrench it free, and then a great push, with the weight of the bear on it, to shove it out so that it went crashing down into the room below. The bear tumbled lightly, like a cat, curling himself into a ball and rolling over and over, unhurt, as the ladder came down. He looked up at them, and there was still something so comic in his expression that they dared, finally, to laugh at him, loud and long.

He paid very little attention to them, once he found that he could not climb up to where they were. He poked about the room, examining everything with his little sharp eyes and his more dependable and most inquisitive nose. He looked into Martha's dollhouse and upset it; he pushed his nose into their mother's workbasket and spilled all the spools and balls of yarn; he tipped over a milk pan and left a puddle of milk and cream on the clean boards. The neat house began to look as though a tempest had blown through it, and still they could not seem to have any hard feeling against a creature who was only looking about for his supper and was entertaining them so highly as he did it. No matter what he did, the three children could not get tired of watching him, or fail to burst out laughing at every new trick or mishap.

Betty looked up finally and saw that the stars were shining behind the little window in the roof. "Uncle Richard and Aunt Clara will certainly be here soon," she said.

Each of them in that minute was thinking the same thing, although it was Tom who spoke first. "Uncle Richard always has his rifle. When he sees the bear—" Martha set up a wail. "Oh, he couldn't, he mustn't. He shan't shoot our bear."

In spite of all the mischief he had made, the bear had begun to seem like a friend, a playmate who had amused them through an exciting hour. They forgot that he had robbed them of their supper and kept them prisoners up under the roof. Their only thought was how to save him when Uncle Richard came. "If there were only some way he could get out," Betty said. "But the windows are too little, and the door won't blow open."

Tom had an idea. He fumbled in his pocket and drew out a long piece of string. He tied a loop in the end of it, a very small loop. "Are you going to catch the bear with it?" Martha asked in wonder, but he shook his head.

Just opposite where they sat was another beam which ran along the top of the wall of the house. It was just above the door. Tom, by scrambling and swinging, once almost falling, got himself across to the beam, holding to the rafter above. He lowered the cord and tried to hook the loop over the latch of the door. Once he tried and failed; then he attempted it again. The bear began to be interested and came across to sniff at the cord. Tom gave a quick jerk (this time the loop had caught) and lifted the latch. The door swung open, and the bear went shambling out, to disappear in the shadows.

Uncle Richard and Aunt Clara appeared on the threshold only a few minutes later. They were, it may be said, considerably surprised. Tom had dropped down from his perch and had got the ladder into place again. Martha and Betty were just scrambling down into a room whose wild disorder looked like something in a bad dream. In answer to Aunt Clara's shocked exclamation, Betty only answered:

"Oh, that was just the bear! And, Aunt Clara, I know how to make hasty pudding. It was a wonderful one, only I hurried a little too much while I was getting it ready."

Character Theme—Responsibility

Time to Think

1. Why was Betty being left in charge of the house and the other children?
2. What was the only thought that comforted Betty about staying alone?
3. What were Mrs. Stowe's last instructions to Betty?
4. What happened when Betty forgot to bar the door?
5. Why did the children want to get the bear out of the house before their uncle came?
6. The bear in this story was comical. Do you think all bears are harmless?

Almost from the time that Stephen Foster was born on the Fourth of July in 1826, he had a special love and talent for music. During his lifetime, he composed almost two hundred songs; at least twenty-five of them have become American folk songs. His songs are full of the spirit of pioneers. "Oh, Susanna!" became the song of the "forty-niners" on their way to California, and today it is considered the theme song of the gold rush and the slogan of the pioneers. You probably recognize the titles of some of his other songs: "Camptown Races," "Old Folks at Home," "My Old Kentucky Home," "Beautiful Dreamer."

Oh, Susanna!

Stephen Foster

I come from Alabama with my banjo on my knee,
I'm going to Louisiana,
My true love for to see.
It rained all night the day I left
The weather was so dry,
The sun so hot I froze to death,
Susanna, don't you cry.

Chorus
Oh, Susanna! Oh, don't you cry for me,
For I come from Alabama with my banjo on my knee.

I had a dream the other night,
When everything was still.
I thought I saw Susanna
A-coming down the hill.
The buckwheat cake was in her mouth,
The tear was in her eye,
Says I, "I'm coming from the South."
Susanna, don't you cry.

I soon will be in New Orleans,
And then I'll look all 'round,
And when I find Susanna,
I'll fall upon the ground.
But if I do not find her,
I think I'll surely die,
And when I'm dead and buried,
Susanna, don't you cry.

157

This American folk song was adopted in
1947 as the state song of Kansas. As you read,
picture the golden prairies and rolling green
hills that are symbolic of America's heartland.

Home on
the Range

Oh, give me a home where the buffalo roam,
Where the deer and the antelope play,
Where seldom is heard a discouraging word
And the skies are not cloudy all day.

Home, home on the range,
Where the deer and the antelope play;
Where seldom is heard a discouraging word
And the skies are not cloudy all day.

Where the air is so pure, the zephyrs so free,
The breezes so balmy and light,
That I would not exchange my home on the range
For all of the cities so bright.

zephyrs—*gentle winds*   **balmy**—*gentle and pleasant*

How often at night when the heavens are bright
With the light from the glittering stars,
Have I stood here amazed and asked as I gazed
If their glory exceeds that of ours.

Oh, I love these wild flowers in this dear land of ours,
The curlew I love to hear scream,
And I love the white rocks and the antelope flocks
That graze on the mountaintops green.

Oh, give me a land where the bright diamond sand
Flows leisurely down the stream;
Where the graceful white swan goes gliding along
Like a maid in a heavenly dream.

Then I would not exchange my home on the range,
Where the deer and the antelope play;
Where seldom is heard a discouraging word
And the skies are not cloudy all day.

    Home, home on the range,
    Where the deer and the antelope play;
    Where seldom is heard a discouraging word
    And the skies are not cloudy all day.

---

curlew—*a bird with long legs
and a curved bill*

Joel Chandler Harris is best remembered for his Uncle Remus stories. The fables are told by an old black man, Uncle Remus, to a seven-year-old boy. These stories often teach some kind of lesson. The main character is Brer (brother) Rabbit, who uses his wits to escape his enemy Brer Fox.

Brer Rabbit, He's a Good Fisherman

Joel Chandler Harris

"Brer Rabbit and Brer Fox were like some children that I know," said Uncle Remus, regarding the little boy, who had come to hear another story, with an affectation of great solemnity. "Both of 'em were always after one another, a prankin' and a pestrin' around. But Brer Rabbit did have some peace because Brer Fox had gotten skittish about puttin' the clamps on Brer Rabbit.

"One day, when Brer Rabbit, and Brer Fox, and Brer Coon, and Brer Bear, and a whole lot of 'em were clearing up a new ground for to plant 'em a roastin'-ear patch, the sun commenced to get sorta hot, and Brer Rabbit got tired. But he didn't let on, 'cause he was afraid the rest of 'em would call him lazy. He just kept on carryin' off trash and pilin' up brush, 'til by-and-by he hollered out that

---

affectation—*a certain display of false behavior*
solemnity—*seriousness*

skittish—*uneasy*
roastin'-ear—*corn*
commenced—*began*

he had a brier in his hand—and then he slipped off, and hunted for a cool place to rest. He looked around for a spell, and after awhile he came across a well with a bucket hangin' on it.

"'That looks cool,' says Brer Rabbit, says he, 'an' cool I expect she is. I'll just get right in there and take me a nap.' And with that he jumped in the bucket he did. But he had hardly started to make himself comfortable than the bucket started to go down into the well."

"Wasn't the Rabbit scared, Uncle Remus?" asked the little boy.

"Honey, there has never been a worse scared beast since the world began than this same Brer Rabbit. He was fairly shakin' all over. He knew where he came from, but he didn't know where he was goin'. Pretty soon he felt the bucket hit the water and there she sat and floated. But Brer Rabbit kept mighty still because he didn't know what minute was going to be his last. He just lay there in the bucket and he shook and he shivered.

"Now Brer Fox he always has one eye on Brer Rabbit, and when he saw that scamp sneak off from the new ground, Brer Fox he sneaked right after him. He knew Brer Rabbit was up to some project or other, and Brer Fox crept off to watch him. Brer Fox saw Brer Rabbit come to the well and stop, and then he saw him jump into the bucket, and then—lo and behold—he saw him go down right out of sight. Well, sir, Brer Fox was the most astonished Fox that you've ever laid eyes on. He sat out there in the bushes and he studied and he studied, but didn't make head nor tails of this kind of business.

---

scamp—*rascal*

"Then he says to himself, says he, 'Well, if this don't bang my times,' says he. 'Right down there in that well is where Brer Rabbit keeps his money hid. And if it isn't that, then he's gone and discovered a gold mine. And if it isn't that, then I'm going to see what it is in there,' says he.

"Brer Fox crept up a little nearer, he did, and he listened, but he didn't hear any fuss. And he kept on creepin' and gettin' nearer and yet he didn't hear anything down in the well. By-and-by he got right up close and peeped down, but he didn't see anything and he didn't hear anything.

"Now all this time Brer Rabbit was mighty near scared out of his skin. He was afraid to move because the bucket might turn right over and spill him out in the water.

"And while he was down there saying his prayers like a train of cars running down a track, old Brer Fox hollered out, 'Heyo, Brer Rabbit! Who you visitin' down there?' says he.

"'Who? Me? Oh, I'm just a fishing, Brer Fox,' says Brer Rabbit, says he. 'I just said to myself that I'd sorta surprise you all with a mess of fish for dinner, and so here I am, and there's the fish. I'm a fishing for suckers, Brer Fox,' says Brer Rabbit, says he.

"'Are there many of them down there, Brer Rabbit?' says Brer Fox, says he.

"'Lots of 'em, Brer Fox. Scores and scores of them. The water is just naturally alive with 'em. Come down and help me haul 'em in, Brer Fox,' says Brer Rabbit, says he.

"'How am I goin' to get down, Brer Rabbit?'

"'Jump in the other bucket hangin' up there, Brer Fox. It'll fetch you down all safe an' sound.'

"Brer Rabbit talked so happy and talked so sweet that Brer Fox jumped right in the bucket, he did. And as he went down, of course his weight pulled Brer Rabbit up. When they passed one another at the halfway place, Brer Rabbit sang out:

"'Good-by, Brer Fox, take care of your clothes,
For this is the way the world goes;
Some go up and some go down,
You'll get to the bottom all safe an' sound.'

"Soon as Brer Rabbit got out, he galloped right off and told the folks that Brer Fox was down in there muddyin' up the drinkin' water. And then he galloped back to the well and hollered down to Brer Fox:

"'Here come a man with a great big gun—
When he hauls you up, you jump an' run.'"

"What then, Uncle Remus?" asked the little boy, as the old man paused.

163

"In just about half an hour, honey, both of 'em were back in the new ground workin' like they had never heard of a well—except that every now and then Brer Rabbit would burst out in a laugh, and old Brer Fox would get a spell of the dry grins."

Character Theme—Resourcefulness

Time to Think

1. How did Brer Rabbit end up in the well?
2. Why did Brer Fox think Brer Rabbit had disappeared into the well?
3. What did Brer Rabbit tell Brer Fox he was doing in the well?
4. How did Brer Rabbit get out of the well?
5. What part does Uncle Remus play in this story?

Spirituals such as this song were sung many years ago by slaves. No one knows their exact origin, because they were carried from plantation to plantation and from state to state. Booker T. Washington said, "No race has ever sung so sweetly, or with such perfect charity, while looking forward to the 'year of Jubilee.'"

Swing Low, Sweet Chariot

Swing low, sweet chariot,
Comin' for to carry me home,
Swing low, sweet chariot,
Comin' for to carry me home.

I look'd over Jordan an' what did I see,
Comin' for to carry me home,
A band of angels comin' after me,
Comin' for to carry me home.

If you get there before I do,
Comin' for to carry me home,
Tell all my friends I'm comin' there too,
Comin' for to carry me home.

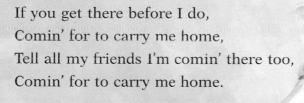

It often takes more courage to face ridicule than a cannon.

Ross Carson's Courage

Author Unknown

Shouting, laughing, pushing against each other, the boys rushed out of the schoolhouse pell-mell.

"Look out, Ross Carson," shouted Tom Lane, in a tone of pretended alarm, "there's a spider on the fountain handle. Run, quick, it may bite you."

There was a roar of laughter at this would-be witty remark, and the eyes of a score or more of thoughtless boys were bent upon the figure of a slender, delicate-looking lad who had been one of the first to get out, and who had approached the fountain for the purpose of getting a drink.

His face flushed painfully as Tom's jest fell on his ear, and the hand that held the handle trembled perceptibly, and his lips scarcely touched the water.

"Oh, he'll stand anything

---

jest—*mocking remark*
perceptibly—*noticeably*

rather than double up his little fist," cried Tom, and, crowding close to Ross, he deliberately knocked the books from under his arm. The slender lad's face flushed at the insult, but he said nothing. He stooped, picked the books up, and then walked on again.

He was quite aware of Tom Lane's great anxiety to pick a quarrel with him, but was determined to give him no excuse for doing so. For Ross knew that he could not with safety enter into any trial of strength with a boy so much older than himself. His lungs were weak, and the doctor had said they could bear no strain whatever. But it was hard to be called a coward, to bear insults of every description without open resentment, to feel that he was looked upon with contempt by his companions, because no taunts or sneers could induce him to fight. And he was too sensitive and shy to explain to them his reasons for not doing so, knowing well that his explanation would be greeted with ridicule and laughter. So he bore his various trials in silence, and not even his mother knew what he endured.

He did not know that this forbearance showed that he possessed true heroism, for, like most boys, he had a strong admiration for deeds of daring and saw little merit in silent endurance.

Tom Lane was the most daring boy among them all. He boasted that he had the coolest head, the strongest arm, and the greatest amount of courage of any fellow of his age in Hillsboro; and none disputed his claim. He was always ready for a fight, and generally came off victor in

contempt—*disrespect and anger*   disputed—*argued*
forbearance—*tolerance*

any contest. He had no pity for weakness, no charity for timidity, and thought all those who feared him fair game for his powers of teasing. Ross might have been fairly treated by the other students but for Tom, who was never weary of exciting enmity against him, and, understanding how to magnify the smallest trifles, was always showing him up as "the biggest coward in Hillsboro Academy."

But retribution was near at hand.

A new town hall was being built in Hillsboro; and a very high, imposing building it was to be, with a steeple second to none. Tom Lane heard his father, who was the contractor for the building, say that a magnificent view could be obtained from this half-completed steeple, and the next day, at the noon recess, Tom proposed to half a dozen of his young friends to go up and take a look for themselves.

"I have a pass from Father," he said, "and the carpenters won't make any fuss."

The ascent to the steeple was easily made, for narrow, winding stairs led up to it; and the boys soon attained a height that made their heads swim as they looked down, breathless, and saw how small appeared the people on the pavement below.

"A good place for a suicide," said Tom as he leaned out.

"Do be careful," said a low voice in a tone of entreaty, and, looking around, the boys saw Ross Carson standing near. He had come up the stairs unnoticed.

"How came you here, you little coward?" asked Tom.

---

retribution—*payment*
imposing—*having a large and powerful appearance*

ascent—*the act going up*
entreaty—*an earnest request*

"The carpenter gave me leave to come up," answered Ross, quietly. "I did not know any one was up here, and I was anxious to see the view. But it is a dangerous place."

"It's likely you think so," sneered Tom. "You'd find the head of a barrel a dangerous place. As for me, I'd like to see the place where I wouldn't go! Boys, do you see that?"

He pointed to a scaffolding which had been erected about the steeple for the use of the workmen. It projected several feet, and overhung the vast chasm below.

"We see it; but what of it?" asked Louis Raymond.

"You'll see what of it," answered Tom. "It's a jolly place to dance a hornpipe." And before his companions could realize his intention, he had climbed out upon the scaffolding and was walking fearlessly about it.

The boys stared in sheer amazement at such recklessness, and begged him to be careful. Their fears for his safety only made Tom more anxious to show his boasted courage, and he began rather a feeble imitation of a sailor's hornpipe.

"Wouldn't it be a long jump to the pavement?" he said.

As he spoke, he looked down, a fatal thing; for his head, which had until now been so cool and steady, began to whirl strangely. He could not remove his eyes from the awful chasm below him. It seemed to fascinate him.

The boys looked at each other in horror. They saw the terrible danger which threatened him. He stood in a kind of stupor, looking down into the fascinating gulf, his eyes wild and staring, his face white with terror. He,

---

scaffolding—*raised platforms from which work is done at great heights*

chasm—*a deep opening*
hornpipe—*a lively dance*

too, knew the awful danger in which he stood, but he was powerless to help himself. The slightest change of position, even the raising of his eyes, and he would  fall. The gulf seemed to be drawing him on; his brain grew more numb with every instant, and his eyes seemed started from their sockets. Back of him shuddered his horror-stricken comrades waiting in an agony of suspense for the fatal end of this terrible drama. Before and below him yawned the great chasm, at the bottom of which the people moving along looked like dwarfs.

Suddenly there was a movement among the boys, and Ross Carson, with white face and set teeth, climbed quickly and noiselessly out of the steeple onto the scaffolding, and with steady step approached the boy who stood on the brink of such a fearful death.

"If he touches him Tom will fall," whispered Louis Raymond.

Low as the whisper was, Ross heard it, and half turned his head toward Louis, pausing an instant, as if to think. Then he made a quick, firm step forward, and throwing both arms around Tom's waist, dragged him backward.

It was all over in an instant. In the face of a fearful and imminent danger, Ross saved his enemy, and slowly, carefully, for every step was peril, drew him back to the steeple, and with the help of the other boys got him inside once more, white as a corpse, it is true, and utterly unnerved, but safe.

There was little said by anyone. In silence Ross helped Tom descend the winding stair, and then walked home as quickly as possible.

"I don't feel well enough to go to school again this afternoon," he said to his mother, "so I'll weed out your flower beds for you."

"You are pale," said Mrs. Carson. "I'm afraid you study too hard."

Ross did not answer, but threw off his coat and began to weed the beds, hoping by hard work to overcome the nervousness which had possessed him ever since leaving the new town hall. He was still weeding a couple of hours later, when he heard the tramp of many feet, and, looking up, he saw about a dozen of his schoolmates, coming in at the little wooden gate, Tom Lane first of all.

"I've come to ask your forgiveness, Ross Carson," said Tom, holding out his hand. "You've taught me this day what true courage is, and made me see what a cowardly sneak I've been."

Tom's lips quivered as he made this humiliating confession, and his eyes were moist with the tears which he

---

imminent—*about to happen*

could restrain with only the greatest effort. Ross took the proffered hand in a warm and hearty grasp as he said: "I'd have done as much for anyone, Tom. Don't make so much of it. But I'm out and out glad to be friends with you."

And friends, fast and true, they were from that time forth; and no one ever again even whispered that Ross Carson lacked courage.

---

proffered—*offered*

Character Theme—Courage & Forgiveness

God's Word Says   *Matthew 5:44*

Love your enemies, bless them that curse you, do good to them that hate you, and pray for them which despitefully use you, and persecute you.

Time to Think

1. Why did the boys think Ross was a coward?
2. Why did Tom go out on the scaffolding of the steeple?
3. How did Ross save Tom's life?
4. What one kind thing did Tom do in the story?
5. How did Ross show true courage?

YOUR REPUTATION

J. L. Nichols

Learn to be a man of your word. One of the most disheartening of all things is to be compelled to do business with a person whose promise is not to be depended upon. There are plenty of people in this wide world whose promise is as slender a tie as a spider's web. Let your given word be as a hempen cord, a chain of wrought steel that will bear the heaviest strain. It will go far in making a man of you, and a real man is the noblest work of God. The man who does not honorably meet his promises is not only dishonest but is also a coward; the man who dares not meet his obligations in good faith can frame no other excuse than that of cowardice.

Young man, have a character of your own. Do not be a lump of moist putty molded and shaped by the influence and impressions of those whom you last met. Your reputation is made up by your conduct. Cultivate force, energy, self-reliance and be a positive quantity that can be counted upon at all times and at all places. Be a man whose word is worth a hundred cents on a dollar and your reputation will be as good as gold.

---

hempen—*like a tough fiber*

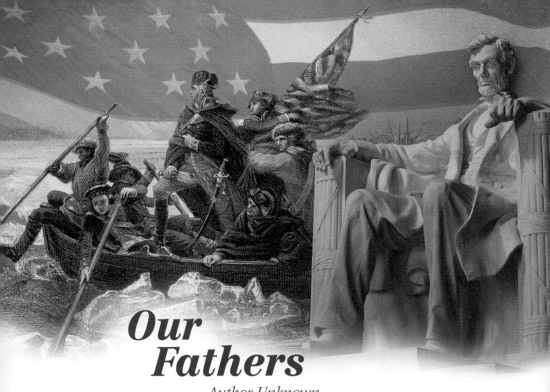

Our Fathers

Author Unknown

Our fathers were high-minded men,
  who firmly kept the faith,
To freedom and to conscience true
  in danger and in death.
Nor should their deeds be e'er forgot,
  for noble men were they,
Who struggled hard for sacred rights,
  and bravely won the day.

And such as our forefathers were, may we,
  their children, be,
And in our hearts their spirit live,
  that baffled tyranny.
Then we'll uphold the cause of right,
  the cause of mercy too;
To toil or suffer for the truth
  is the noblest thing to do.

---

baffled—*confused, obstructed*
tyranny—*abusive exercise of power*

Washington

Nancy Byrd Turner

He played by the river when he was young,
He raced with rabbits along the hills,
He fished for minnows, and climbed and swung,
And hooted back at the whippoorwills.
Strong and slender and tall he grew—
And then, one morning, the bugles blew.

Over the hills the summons came,
Over the river's shining rim.
He said that the bugles called his name,
He knew that his country needed him,
And he answered, "Coming!" and marched away
For many a night and many a day.

Perhaps when the marches were hot and long
He'd think of the river flowing by
Or, camping under the winter sky,
Would hear the whippoorwill's far-off song.
Boy and soldier, in peace or strife,
He loved America all his life!

---

summons—*a call to come*

The glory of life is to love, not to be loved;
to give, not to get; to serve, not to be served.

The Girl Who Saved the Stockade

Author Unknown

One evening in autumn, in the year 1776, there came bad news to a little settlement on the banks of the Ohio River, near where the city of Wheeling now stands.

A scout who had been sent into the forest to learn what danger lurked in the neighborhood reported that the Indians were on the warpath.

He had heard their terrible whoops, had seen a smoldering blockhouse which they had burned, and had watched a party of them as, daubed with war paint and bristling with feathers, they moved swiftly in single file along a forest trail.

---

smoldering—*burning slowly without flames or smoke*

daubed—*smeared*

"To the stockade!" cried Colonel Sheppard, when he heard the evil tidings. But the settlers were already leaving their cabins and walking quickly and silently towards the log fort, which was their only protection.

As the men, women, and children passed through the gate, two captains, Silas and Ebenezer Zane by name, stood by, making sure that none were missing.

It was not long before a war whoop was heard in the forest, and the fight began. The woods seemed full of Indians. They outnumbered the men and boys in the fort five to one.

But the women and girls counted for something in the fights of those days. While the men and boys, as sharpshooters, thrust their long rifles through the loopholes, the women and girls were by no means idle. For there were bullets to be cast from the molten lead. There were the guns, overheated from rapid firing, to be cooled, reloaded, and passed to the men at the loopholes.

A day and a night wore slowly away. Without food or sleep, and almost without water, these brave men, women and young people stood their posts.

Again and again the Indians made a rush, under cover of smoke, to storm the fort or to set it on fire. Each time they were driven back.

After the last attack, when they had retired into the woods to plan some new mischief, Colonel Sheppard called a council of war.

"The powder has almost given out," he said. "There is not enough for half a dozen rounds."

---

cast—*molded*

molten lead—*lead that is melted into liquid*

177

The settlers looked at one another very soberly. What could even the bravest do without powder?

"There's a keg of powder in my cabin," said Captain Ebenezer Zane, "but it is sixty yards away."

To cross that space before the eyes of those Indians meant death.

Yes, but the Indians were sure to come back and make another attack. The settlers must have powder, or give up the fort. If they surrendered, the men would be tortured at the stake, and the women and children taken into captivity or put to death.

"We must have powder," said the colonel to his men; "and there's none nearer than Captain Zane's cabin. Who will volunteer?"

Every man and boy in that band of heroes wished to go.

"No, no, indeed! Not a man shall go; we haven't one to spare. Let me go!" cried Elizabeth Zane, a fair young girl, sister of Captain Zane.

In vain they tried to keep her back.

"No, Betty, you must not run the risk!" cried all the men; "you'll be killed!"

"Besides, Betty, you can't run fast enough; you are only a girl," said a boy.

"But I am going," Elizabeth said. "You have wasted too much time already. Look at those Indians creeping out of the woods."

The men and boys looked ashamed.

"Let me go; I can run as fast as any of you," said the girl. "If I am killed, I shall not be missed as a man would be. Somebody pin up my hair, so it won't be loose for the Indians to catch hold of."

Carefully the big gate was opened just wide enough for Elizabeth to slip out. She gave one loving look at her brothers. Her dark eyes were shining, but in her face there was not a sign of fear as she walked slowly across the open space to her brother's log cabin.

The Indians hiding in the bushes saw the gate open and gazed in wonder to see the girl, bareheaded, and with sleeves rolled up, quietly walk out of the fort as if for a morning stroll.

"Squaw! squaw!" they shouted, but did not fire a shot.

Elizabeth had now reached the cabin and found the keg of powder.

In breathless silence the watchers at the loopholes saw the girl appear in the doorway with the keg of powder clasped in her arms. She stopped a moment and gave a quick glance at the fort, which seemed a long way off.

"Now it is death to my poor sister! Why did we ever let her go?" said Zanc, as he saw the young girl making ready to run back.

Pulling her skirts tight around her, and hugging the keg, Elizabeth started for the fort as fast as she could run.

The Indians set up a yell. They knew now what the girl was doing.

Crack! crack! crack! sounded the rifles of the Indians.

The bullets whistled past her, but not one hit her. Almost at the gate, the excited girl stumbled and fell.

Was she hit?

No.

She picked herself up and ran for her life.

Ping! ping! sang the bullets; but in another moment the great gate was opened, and Elizabeth fell into the arms of her brother, who stood ready to catch her.

"Three cheers for Betty Zane!" cried the colonel, and they were given with a will.

With Elizabeth unharmed, and plenty of powder, they all took fresh courage.

The worst, however, was over. Before sunrise the next morning, mounted riflemen from other settlements came to the help of the fort. The Indians now gave up hope. After killing the livestock and setting fire to some cabins, they hurried across the Ohio.

Twenty years afterward, Captain Ebenezer Zane founded the town of Zanesville, Ohio, which is now a flourishing city.

As for his brave sister, she kept the beauty of her youth even to old age. She lived to tell the story of the gunpowder to her grandchildren.

"But never," said one young girl who heard the story from her lips, "did she speak of it boastfully or as a wonderful matter."

Character Theme—Courage & Sacrifice

Time to Think

1. How did the scout know the Indians were on the warpath?
2. How did the women and girls help during the battle?
3. Why did Betty insist on running for the gunpowder?
4. When did the Indians begin to shoot at Betty?
5. Which of these words best describe Betty Zane— unselfish, courageous, athletic, honest?

SOMEBODY SAID IT COULDN'T BE DONE

Edgar A. Guest

Somebody said that it couldn't be done,
　　But he with a chuckle replied
That "maybe it couldn't," but he would be one
　　Who wouldn't say so till he'd tried.
So he buckled right in with a trace of a grin
　　On his face. If he worried he hid it.
He started to sing as he tackled the thing
　　That couldn't be done, and he did it.

Somebody scoffed: "Oh, you'll never do that;
　　At least no one ever has done it;"
But he took off his coat and he took off his hat,
　　And the first thing we knew, he'd begun it.
With a lift of the chin and a bit of a grin,
　　Without any doubting or quiddit,
He started to sing as he tackled the thing
　　That couldn't be done, and he did it.

There are thousands to tell you it cannot be done,
　　There are thousands to prophesy failure,
There are thousands to point out to you, one by one,
　　The dangers that wait to assail you.
But just buckle in with a bit of a grin,
　　Just take off your coat and go to it;
Just start to sing as you tackle the thing
　　That "cannot be done," and you'll do it.

quiddit—*quibbling*

The Map Maker

Dorothy Brown Thompson

In Genoa long years ago
    An old map maker wrought with art
The way tall ships and seamen go
    On many a labored chart.

And looking for a prentice lad
    He found one Christopher, who seemed
Exact and careful, though he had
    The eyes of one who dreamed.

His master would have frowned, perhaps,
    To know his lad would chart so true
That half the world and all the maps
    Must soon be drawn anew!

Genoa (jĕn′ō·ə)—*a city in Italy*
prentice lad—*a boy who serves as an apprentice*

Trouble is opportunity in work clothes.
W. Clement Stone

Clara Barton

Grace Humphrey

Clarissa Harlowe Barton was born on December 25, 1821, in an old farmhouse in Worcester County, Massachusetts. Her grandfather had fought through the War for Independence, and her father had been in Mad Anthony Wayne's campaigns against the Indians. Clara listened to many a stirring story of the dangers they had met. As they fought their battles over again, she learned her country's history and loved it passionately.

The older Barton children were her teachers, and very rapidly indeed she learned. For she went to school at three, able to spell many words of three syllables but so shy that she could not answer questions. Her athletic brother David, whom she admired greatly, taught her to ride.

"Learning to ride is just learning a horse," said he.

"How can I learn a horse?" asked the little sister.

"Just feel that the horse is a part of yourself, the big half for the time being. Here, hold fast by the mane," and David lifted her up to a colt's back, sprang on another himself, and away they galloped down the pasture—a mad ride which they repeated often, till she learned to stick on. In after years when she rode strange horses in a trooper's saddle for all-night gallops to safety, she was grateful to David for those wild rides among the colts.

Strong in body, alert in mind, Clara Barton grew up, never free from shyness unless she was busily at work. "The only real fun is doing things," she would say. She helped milk and churn, and she learned to drive a nail straight.

When she was eleven, David was seriously injured by a fall from the roof of a new barn. For two years he was an invalid. At once Clara took charge of the sickroom. She changed from a lively child, fond of outdoor sports, to a nurse, calm and cheerful, no matter how exacting the doctors' orders were, no matter how much David was suffering. The sickroom was kept tidy and quiet. Clara was clear-headed and always at her post. Nothing was too hard for her to do well if it would make her brother more comfortable. During those two years she did not have even one half holiday.

---

exacting—*requiring careful attention*

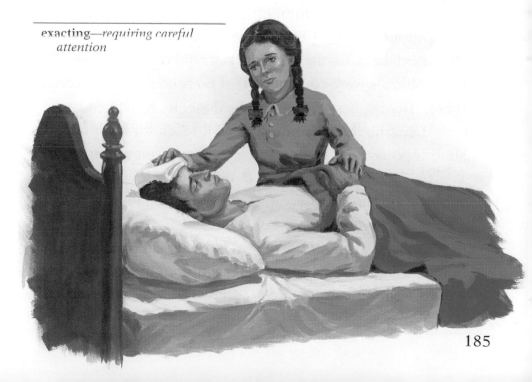

"That child's a born nurse," the neighbors would say. And the doctors, agreeing, praised her tenderness and patience. But these two years made her more sensitive and self-conscious. Her shyness made her a real problem to her mother.

"Give her some responsibility," advised a wise family friend; "give her a school to teach. For others she will be fearless."

Far ahead of girls of her age in her studies, at fifteen Clara Barton put up her hair and lengthened her skirts and went to face her forty pupils. "It was one of the most awful moments in my life," she said long afterwards. "I could not find my voice; my hand trembled so much that I was afraid to turn the page. But the end of the first day proved that I could do it."

Her pluck and strength won the respect of the big rough boys, who found that she was as sturdy as they. The school was a great success, and for sixteen years she taught, winter and summer.

In Bordentown, New Jersey, no school was possible, she heard, because the children ran wild on the streets. The town officials were convinced that no school could succeed there. Here was something to be done; it challenged her!

"Give me three months, and I'll teach for nothing," she proposed, her eyes flashing with determination.

In a tumble-down old building she began with six rough children from the streets, each of whom at the end of the day became an enthusiastic advertisement for the new teacher. At the close of the school year she had an assistant, because there were six hundred children on the rolls. A large new building was erected, the first public school in the state. For Clara Barton had a gift for teaching, as well as a spirit of enthusiasm.

When her voice gave out, she went to Washington for a rest and secured a position in the patent office. So she was at the capital when the conflict long threatening between North and South developed into war. Fort Sumter was fired on. The time for sacrifice had come.

In response to Lincoln's call for volunteers, Massachusetts sent men immediately. On the historic nineteenth of April one regiment was attacked in the streets of Baltimore by an angry crowd. With many wounded, their train finally reached Washington and was met by a number of sympathetic women, Clara Barton among them. In the group of injured soldiers she recognized some of her old pupils and friends. At the infirmary she helped dress their wounds. Nothing was ready for such an emergency. Handkerchiefs gave out. Women rushed to their homes and tore up sheets for bandages.

This was Clara Barton's first experience in caring for wounded soldiers. She wanted them to have the necessities and all the comforts that were possible. So she put an advertisement in a Worcester paper, asking for supplies and money for the wounded men, and stating that she would give out whatever was sent. The response of Massachusetts was overwhelming. The food and clothing filled her apartment to overflowing, and she had to rent space in a warehouse.

This work made a new person of the shy Clara Barton who had been a bundle of fears. This was no time to be self-conscious. Here was a great need, and she knew that she had the ability to meet it.

South of Washington battles were going on. Transports left each day with provisions for the army of the Potomac, returning with a load of wounded soldiers. Clara Barton went to the docks to meet them. She moved about, bandaging here, giving medicine there, feeding those weak from lack of nourishment, and writing letters home. She was sick at heart when she saw men who had lain on the damp ground for hours with a fever, so that her dressings and tender care were too late.

If only wounds could be attended to as soon as the soldiers fell in battle, she realized, hundreds of deaths could be prevented. She must go to the front, to the very firing line, even though it was against all army regulations and against public sentiment. For many weeks she met only rebuffs and refusals, always the same reply: "No, the battlefield is no place for a woman. It is full of danger!"

True—but how great was the need of the men at the front! Help must be brought to them when they fell. When she laid her plan before her father, he said, "If you believe this is your duty, you must go to the front. You need not fear harm. Every true soldier will respect and bless you."

From that time on, she determined to keep trying until she received permission. At last she was able to put her request to General Rucker, asking him for a pass to the battle front. "I have the supplies. Give me a way to reach the men," she begged.

"You must think of the dangers this work will bring you. At any time you may be under the fire of guns."

---

public sentiment—*the general opinion*   rebuffs—*refusals*

188

"But I am the daughter of a soldier; I am not afraid of the battlefield." She described to him the condition of the men when they reached Washington and added earnestly, "I must go to the front to care for them quickly."

The passport was given her, and through the weary years of the war she stayed at her post—giving medicine to the sick, stimulants to the wounded and dying, nourishing food to men faint from loss of blood. Working under no society or leader, she was free to come and go. On sixteen battlefields, during the hot summer days of the siege of Charleston, all through the Wilderness Campaign, in the Richmond hospitals, there was no limit to her service. And from her first day on the firing line she had the confidence of the officers and their help and encouragement. Wherever there were wounded soldiers who had been under her care, Clara Barton's name was spoken with affection.

stimulants—*medications that aid alertness*

In so far as was possible, she was told in advance about battles that were being planned, so that she might be ready with her supplies. At Antietam, while shot was falling around the group of workers, she ordered her wagons driven to an old farmhouse just back of the lines. Between the tall rows of corn, into the barnyard, the worst cases were carried. For lack of medical supplies the surgeons had been using bandages of corn husks.

Her supplies quickly unloaded, Clara Barton hurried out to revive the wounded, giving them bread soaked in wine. The supply of bread ran out; she had only three cases of wine left. "Open them," she commanded; "give us that, and God help us!" For faster and faster the wounded soldiers were coming in. She watched the men open the cases. What was that packed around the bottles? Cornmeal! It could not have been worth more if it had been gold dust. In the farmhouse they found kettles. She mixed the cornmeal with water and soon was making great quantities of gruel. All night long she helped carry this hot food up and down the rows of wounded soldiers.

On one of these trips she met a surgeon, tired and disheartened. He had only one short candle left, and if men's lives were to be saved, the doctors must work all night. "Heartless neglect and carelessness," he stormed. But Miss Barton had four boxes of candles in her stores, ready for just such an emergency.

Near that battlefield at Antietam she remained until all her supplies were gone. "If we had had more wagons," she reported to General Rucker, "we could have cared for all the wounded soldiers."

---

gruel—*thin porridge made by boiling cornmeal in water or milk*

"You shall have enough the next time," he responded. And the government, recognizing the value of her service, gave her ten wagons with drivers and sixty mules.

When the drivers were rebellious and sulky because they were forced to serve under the orders of a woman, she controlled them just as she had controlled the rough boys in her New Jersey school. Once she prepared a hot dinner and asked them to share it. After she had cleared away the dishes, the men came up to her, awkward and self-conscious.

"Come and get warm," she welcomed them.

"No'm, we didn't come for that," said the leader. "We come to tell you we're ashamed. Truth is, lady, we didn't want to drive these wagons. We knew there was fightin' ahead for us to do, an' we never saw a train of wagons with a woman in charge before. Now, we've been mean and contrary all day long, and here you've treated us like a general and his staff. It's the best meal we've had in two years, and we shan't trouble you again."

The next morning they brought her a steaming hot breakfast. For six months they stayed with her, through battles and marches, through snow and heat, a devoted corps of assistants, always ready for her orders. They helped her nurse the sick and dress the wounded. And day by day they themselves grew kinder.

Once Clara Barton worked for five days and nights with only three hours of sleep. Often in danger, it seemed as though she were protected by some special charm so that she might save the lives of others.

She gave her help to men who had fought on either side. They were suffering, and they needed her; that was enough. She went over to Fredericksburg, where every stone wall was a blazing line of battle. A regiment came marching down the road. She stepped aside. The general saw her and leaned from his saddle to say: "You're in great danger, madam. Do you want protection?"

"Thank you, but I think—" Clara Barton looked at the ranks of soldiers marching past—"I think, sir, I'm the best protected woman in the United States!"

"That's so, that's so!" cried out the men as they gave her a great cheer that was taken up by line after line until it sounded like the cheering after a victory.

"I believe you're right, madam," said the general, bowing low.

Over the battlefield a sharp wind was blowing. The suffering men lay shivering and half frozen in the bitter cold. Some were found famished under the snow. Clara Barton had all the wounded brought to one place and great fires built. But these fires did not give enough heat to warm them. What to do? She discovered an old chimney not far away. "Tear it down," she ordered; "heat the bricks and place them around the men." Soon she had kettles of coffee and gruel steaming over the fires, and thus saved many lives.

As the war drew to an end, President Lincoln received hundreds of letters from anxious parents asking for news of their boys. The list of missing totaled sixty thousand. In despair the President sent for Clara Barton, thinking she had more information than anyone else, and asked her to take up the task. A four-years' task it proved to be. She copied infirmary and burial lists. She studied records of prisons and hospitals. She succeeded in tracing and sending definite word about thirty thousand men. Through the whole country her name became a household word.

Her strong will had held her body to its work during the long war, and afterwards for the task of tracing missing men. Then the doctors insisted that she must rest and sent her to Switzerland for a change of scene. After a month, when she was beginning to feel some improvement, she had callers one day who represented the International Red Cross Society.

"What is that?" asked Clara Barton.

And they explained how a Swiss, visiting the battlefield of Solferino and seeing thousands of wounded soldiers poorly cared for, had planned a society for the relief of soldiers. Its badge, a red cross on a white ground, gave its workers protection from both armies. Red Cross workers helped all persons without regard to their race or religion or uniform. This was exactly the principle on which Clara Barton had been working, and today it is the very heart of the Red Cross plan. Already, these visitors said, twenty-two nations had formed such societies. But the United States, though invited twice, had done nothing. They asked her help.

Three days afterwards the Franco-Prussian War began, and soon Clara Barton was again at the front. With the German army she entered Strasbourg after the siege. On every hand were sick and wounded soldiers and homeless, starving women and children. There she helped the Red Cross Society in its relief work. And this work made her enthusiastic about the Red Cross. For at once she felt the difference. She saw the new society accom-

---

Solferino (sōl'fə·rē'nō)—*an Italian village*
Strasbourg (sträs'bŏŏrg)—*a city in France*

plish in four months, with system and trained workers, what our country had failed to do in four years. What a contrast! Wherever the white flag with the red cross was flying, there were supplies in plenty, prompt attention to wounds, cleanliness and comfort. Wherever she had worked alone, there were mistakes, delays, needless suffering, and lives sacrificed. She said to herself, "When I return to America, I will try to make our people understand what the Red Cross means."

She succeeded, though it was a task of years. She found officials hard to convince, clinging to the tradition that forbade any alliance with foreign countries.

But in March, 1882, the United States organized a Red Cross society. Clara Barton became the first president of the American Red Cross, an office she held for twenty-two years. It was her suggestion that the Red

---

siege—*an attack on a city or fortress by an enemy attempting to capture it*

Cross be prepared to give relief in time of peace as well as war. Through her influence the International Red Cross Conference also adopted this American plan.

Character Theme—Kindness/Service
& Initiative

Time to Think

1. When was Clara able to forget her terrible shyness?
2. What was Clara's first experience as a nurse?
3. How old was Clara when she started teaching forty pupils?
4. During what war did Clara begin caring for wounded soldiers?
5. How did Clara Barton speed up and improve the treatment of wounded soldiers?
6. How is Clara Barton's life an example of resourcefulness?
7. What is Clara Barton most known for in American history?

Compassion

James A. Sanaker

Compassion is love, plus desire to share
The trouble and tears that come from despair;
Compassion is love, plus sympathy, too,
With a will to help, to heal and renew.

Compassion is love, plus pity enough
To walk with the weary when the going is rough;
Compassion is love, plus the spirit to do
For others; our Lord had compassion, do you?

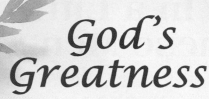

God's Greatness

Psalm 8

O Lord our Lord, how excellent is Thy name in all the earth! Who hast set Thy glory above the heavens.

Out of the mouth of babes and sucklings hast Thou ordained strength because of Thine enemies, that Thou mightest still the enemy and the avenger.

When I consider Thy heavens, the work of Thy fingers, the moon and the stars, which Thou hast ordained;

What is man, that Thou art mindful of him? and the son of man, that Thou visitest him?

For Thou hast made him a little lower than the angels, and hast crowned him with glory and honor.

Thou madest him to have dominion over the works of Thy hands; Thou hast put all things under his feet:

All sheep and oxen, yea, and the beasts of the field;

The fowl of the air, and the fish of the sea, and whatsoever passeth through the paths of the seas.

O Lord our Lord, how excellent is Thy name in all the earth!

---

ordained—*ordered by authority*
avenger—*one who gets revenge*
dominion—*control and authority*

In a Little World These Men Stood Tall

Catherine Otten

Ours was a house divided. At the turn of the twenti-
eth century, our family moved into our brand-new house,
which was divided into a grocery store in the front, and
our home in the back and above the store. It stood on a
corner of the city limits and it soon became the center of
all neighborhood activities.

Being the children of a storekeeper had its advan-
tages. Everyone for blocks around knew us. There was no
generation gap in those days. Other children were not
our only friends. Customers as well as the salesmen and
peddlers who called at our store and worked in the
neighborhood were also our friends. There was the
milkman, the fruitman, the candyman, the iceman, the
ragman, the lamplighter and the policeman.

The best grown-up friend a child had in the neighborhood was the policeman who walked our beat. He was
a big, heavyset, ruddy-faced, jolly Norwegian who lived
down the block. His thick, blond mustache and curly hair
were always precisely and carefully trimmed. In spite
of his size, there was no more dashing a figure of a man
around the neighborhood than he. All of the little girls
had a crush on him.

Immaculately clean and polished, he "reported in"
each morning from the police box on our corner. It was
a six-sided, grayish-blue structure which occupied only
about three square feet. It contained a telephone and a

---

beat—*an assigned area*   **immaculately**—*without imperfection*
dashing—*handsome*

couple of hooks for the policeman's
rain gear. Occasionally, our friend
the policeman would gather a bunch
of giggling kids and lock
them up in his fascinat-
ing little police box.
"We got arrested today,"
they would brag to their
families when they
returned home.

The duties
and respon-
sibilities of a
policeman those
days were simple. Sometimes for weeks, his chief business was watching for broken boards in our wooden
sidewalks as he walked his beat. Finding lost children and
pets seldom taxed his endurance, and mediating family
squabbles and misbehaviors was also part of his responsibility. Our policeman knew every family on his beat, and
he was a friend to all of them.

Perhaps the best-loved man in the lives of a storekeeper's children was the candyman. He arrived weekly
in his pretty, horse-drawn wagon with all the pomp and
flourish of a circus entertainer. He expected an eager
gathering of young admirers, and he was seldom disap-
pointed. Because we were the kids who lived in the store,
we could follow this happy, pudgy, white-haired little man
into the store. The rest of the kids had to be content with
pressing their noses to the window.

---

taxed—*was a burden to*   **pomp and flourish**—*showy display*
mediating—*settling conflicts*

Our candyman was as sweet and good as his merchandise. Sometimes he would consult one of us kids about the merit of some new candy novelty if Mama hesitated to order. I remember well the day he let me choose a little wax bottle of colored syrup for each of my friends outside. The samples paid off. Demand made reordering necessary over and over again. The sweetened wax bottles were drained and then chewed like gum for a long time after.

Some of the candies were "seasonal specials." As Easter drew near, the box of chocolate marshmallow eggs tempted the "gamblers," young and old alike. A customer chose his own egg from the box, and bit into it. If the egg had a pink center he could choose another one free. Of course, he bit into that one too, hoping to find another pink center. The one day that always sold out on "specials" was April Fool's Day. Children saved their pennies for weeks so they could treat their friends to little chocolate-covered wooden caramels, pepper-filled bonbons and chocolate drops filled with cotton.

bonbons—*candies that have soft flavored fillings*

Few people enjoyed their work more than our candy-man. Perhaps it was the warm welcome he received at each stop, or the joy he experienced as he treated his young admirers. Whatever the reason, he was one of the most welcome and cheerful salesmen to peddle his wares at our store.

"Here comes the iceman" was a familiar chant heard in the neighborhood on hot summer days. The iceman, like the policeman, belonged to the neighborhood. The grocery store, the butcher shop and the cafe were his biggest customers, but almost every house also had an icebox in those days.

Like the milkman, the iceman made his rounds, and like the candyman, he had his followers. There was always a thirsty group of kids watching as he chipped away on the huge blocks of ice. In noisy admiration, they would cheer as he caught up the heavy cold block with his iron tongs, hurled it over his shoulder, and lugged it to the waiting wooden icebox. While he was gone, of course, the kids helped themselves to the icy chips, and sucked away in pure delight.

On scorching hot summer days, his groups of free-loaders resembled a little parade, and it lasted until the last block of ice was delivered. Then the iceman, with a generous flourish, would brush the sawdust-covered leftover pieces of melting ice out onto the road for the big scramble.

Gus, the lamplighter, was a daily visitor in the neighborhood. Some child often made the rounds "helping" him light up the corner gas lamps. Gus was a big, rough, happy fellow who came twice a day; early in the morning to put

peddle his wares—*advertise and sell his merchandise*

out the high lights with his long hooked pole, and again late in the afternoon to turn them on again.

Gus limped painfully, so it was not hard for the children to keep up with him as he did his "magic tricks" at each stop. He spoke only German, so even if he tried to explain it remained a mystery to his young fans.

Every now and then the waffleman came around. He announced his arrival by blowing a little trumpet, and that was the only invitation necessary. By the time the waffle wagon got to your house, you were out waiting to spend a nickel for a big, brown, powdered-sugared treat.

The iceman, the waffleman, and the lamplighter no longer exist. Progress has taken them out of the picture. But the memories of them are tucked away in my heart and in the hearts of many others of my generation. They are marked, "Childhood Memories—fragile, handle with care."

Character Theme—Friendship & Gratitude

Time to Think

1. What did the author mean when she said, "Ours was a house divided"?
2. Name some of the grown-up friends of the neighborhood children.
3. Why did candy sell so well around April Fool's Day?
4. Why are there no more lamplighters or icemen?

That May Morning

Leland B. Jacobs

That May morning—very early—
As I walked the city street,
Not a single store was open
Any customer to greet.

That May morning—it was early—
As I walked the avenue,
I could stop and stare and window-shop,
And hear the pigeons coo.

Early, early that May morning
I could skip and jump and run
And make shadows on the sidewalk,
Not disturbing anyone.

All the windows, all the lamp posts,
Every leaf on every tree
That was growing through the sidewalk
Seemed to be there just for me.

Citizenship

William P. Prye

This country of ours is worth our thought, our care, our labor, our lives. What a magnificent country it is! What a Republic for the people, where all are kings! Men of great wealth, of great rank, of great influence can live without difficulty under despotic power; but how can you and I, how can the average man endure the burden it imposes? Oh, this blessed Republic of ours stretches its hand down to men, lifts them up, while despotism puts its heavy hand on their heads and presses them down! This blessed Republic of ours speaks to every boy in the land, black or white, rich or poor, and asks him to come up higher and higher. You remember that boy out here on the prairie, the son of a widowed mother, poor, neglected perhaps by all except the dear old mother. But the Republic did not neglect him. The Republic said to that boy: "Boy, there is a ladder; its foot is on the earth, its top is in the sky. Boy, go up." And the boy mounted that ladder rung by rung; by the rung of the free schools, by the rung of the academy, by the rung of the college, by the rung of splendid service in the United States Army, by the rung of the United States House of Representatives, by the rung of the United States Senate, by the rung of the Presidency of the Great Republic, by the rung of a patient sickness and a heroic death; until James A. Garfield is a name to be forever honored in the history of our country.

Now, is not a Republic like that worth the tribute of our conscience? Is it not entitled to our best thought, to our holiest purpose?

---

despotic—*extremely harsh*

Cap

Georgene Faulkner

Cap did not have a long pedigree; he was just a plain dog. But one look into his honest brown eyes would tell you that Cap was to be trusted. He had character; he could always be depended upon.

From the time that he was a small puppy he had tried to help everyone upon the farm. He guarded the baby as though he were responsible for the child. As the baby toddled about, Cap walked proudly to his side as much as to say, "I will watch him and see that no one harms him." Sometimes, as they lay side by side in the sunny dooryard, the baby would bury both fat fists in Cap's soft coat and try to pull out handfuls of fur, but Cap never growled.

Once the baby fell face downward into the duck pond and would have drowned; but faithful Cap pulled him out of the water. Then, seizing baby's muddy hat in his mouth, he plunged away to the farmhouse, barking and calling for help. "Yere-ere-ere-err-yere-ere, come here, ere-ere," barked Cap. The frightened family followed at his heels and soon brought the half-drowned child into the house.

---

pedigree—*list of ancestors*

"That puppy is truly a captain," said his master. "He knows just what to do." So, from that day, the dog was named Captain and called "Cap."

The whole family loved the bright little dog, but his special friend was Pierre. Pierre, who was twelve years old on the day that Cap was born, felt that Cap was his birthday present. Pierre trained Cap to come at his call and to go out with him to watch and guard the sheep. Every day the boy and his dog wandered across the hills together. Then, when the sheep were ready to come home, Cap barked at their heels and not one of them dared to disobey his sharp command. "Yere-yere, come here-here!" He was like a captain calling his orders to his soldiers, "Fall in! Forward—March!" The sheep would scurry before him down the dusty road.

One day, when they were far up on the hillside, a lamb fell over the rocky side of the ravine and dropped on the ledge below. "Ma-ma-ma," bleated the lamb, as it cried for its mother.

The mother sheep answering, "Baa-baa, baa-aaa-aa," rushed to the side of the hill. The poor mother sheep, however, not knowing how to reach her frightened baby, called loudly for help.

The day was very warm and Pierre, lying down under a tree, had fallen asleep, while the faithful Cap, stretched out at his side, was resting as he watched the sheep grazing peacefully on the hillside. Suddenly Cap sat up, and his ears pricked forward as he heard the call of distress. He ran quickly over the rocks and when he saw the lamb down below he gave a loud sharp bark, as much as to say, "Hold on, we will help you."

He knew that he could not reach the lamb, but he knew that his young master could do so. He ran back under the tree and tugged at Pierre's coat until the sleepy shepherd boy was wide awake.

From Cap's actions, the boy knew that a lamb was in trouble. Seizing his shepherd's staff, he climbed up over the rocks, following the excited dog. Cap led him on with sharp barks until they reached the ledge from which the lamb had fallen.

When Pierre looked down, the ledge was so steep that to think of climbing down made him almost dizzy. What could he do? He must not leave the lamb to die.

Cap looked at his master with eager eyes. Pierre would think of some way, he knew, and he, Cap, would help him. Suddenly, remembering a long, strong rope

which the boy had brought with him, Cap rushed back. With one end of the rope in his mouth and the rest trailing along behind him, he came back to his young master.

"Good dog, Cap!" said Pierre. "The rope—why, of course, that is the only way."

Then, tying one end of the rope to a tree on the top of the hill and the other end around his own body, he lowered himself over the side of the rocks. He took the staff in his hand because he saw that he could not reach the lamb without it. At last he reached the end of the rope and then, leaning far over, he put the staff under the lamb and lifted it up. But, as he looked over the rocky ravine, he wondered how he could climb back with the lamb in his arms. A misstep would mean sure death for them both. Cap was barking wildly overhead and the mother sheep was bleating mournfully. The boy shut his teeth, and, looking up toward the sky, he prayed, "Oh, God, help me!"

Instantly, his prayer was answered, for he knew just what to do. Untying the rope from his body, he tied it around the lamb and, leaning against a scrubby pine tree for support, he called, "Hey, Cap! Hey, Cap!" The dog looked down, and realizing at once that he must work with his teeth, he pulled up the lamb. Then he tugged at the rope until he freed the lamb, and the frightened creature curled up safely by his mother.

With the free end of the rope in his mouth, Cap went to the ledge and dropped it over toward the boy. The rope caught in the branches of the pine tree; but Pierre pulled it down with his staff and tied it securely around his waist. As he began his perilous climb up the rocks, the big dog at the top barked his encouragement.

At last the boy reached the top of the rocks. His clothing was torn and his legs and arms were bruised and bleeding, but he was safe and he knew that the lamb was safe also. Weak and dizzy with a sprained ankle, he fell upon the ground, exhausted. Cap licked the face and hands of his young master and then, when he did not get up and walk, became excited again. He said as plainly as a dog can talk, "Lie here and rest, while I go for help."

Cap took his young master's cap in his teeth and ran down into the valley where the farmer and his older son were reaping. The farmer at once knew that something serious had happened; they followed Cap up the hillside where they found Pierre. The rope, fastened to him, and tied about the tree, together with his bruised body, told them the story.

"My boy," said the father. "You should not have risked your life for a lamb."

"Why, I did not do it alone, Father," said the boy. "Cap knew just what to do and he helped me."

"Good dog, Cap!" said the farmer. He patted the dog on the head, and Cap licked his hand to show that he knew he was appreciated.

Pierre suffered so much from the sprained ankle and from his bruises that for a time he could not watch the flock. But Cap had proved that he could be trusted to look after the sheep. For a while the shepherd dog went out alone to the hillside. When the boy was better, they went out together to take care of the flock. Many happy days they spent wandering over the hills, for the boy and his dog were inseparable friends.

"Cap is my best friend," said Pierre. "He always understands everything I say to him. I know that he loves me and I love him dearly."

The years went on and war came to the peaceful valley. Pierre was now a young man, eighteen years old, and glad that he was to march away and serve his country.

Across the green pastures, ugly trenches were dug and barbed wire coils were tangled everywhere. No sheep were grazing upon the hillside now. They had all been sold and killed for food, while the dog, Captain, had been given to the ambulance corps.

"My son has gone to the front," said the father proudly, "and I shall go too, when I am needed. This shepherd dog, Captain, is his dog. I know that my boy will be glad to have his dog in service, also. He is a good dog, Cap."

Cap was soon trained by the Red Cross Society to search out the wounded upon the battlefield and to bring them help. Cap was very proud of his harness, with its relief supplies and tiny canteens, and of his red cross and badge of service. From the first day, he showed his ability to look after the wounded soldiers.

"That dog is the kindest and most faithful animal in the whole lot," said the young doctor who trained Cap for the service. "The other day Captain saved thirty lives by his persistent searching on the battlefield. We know when Cap comes back, holding a hat in his mouth, that there is someone out there whom we can help, and he leads us to the place at once. Why, that dog almost talks, he is so intelligent."

One day during frightful firing across the trenches, the dogs and men suffered from the deadly fumes of poisonous gas. The doctor put a mask over Cap's face to protect him from the gases. Cap seemed to know that the mask was for his own good and, although he had never worn a muzzle in his life, he did not growl but went right on with his work.

When the firing ceased and the fumes had passed away, the mask was removed from Cap. He ran out into the valley of death, into the "no man's land" of the dead and wounded, and sniffed about to find someone to help. At last he was rewarded by finding a young soldier who was alive. As he sniffed the wounded soldier, his tail wagged in joy and he suddenly broke the law of the Red Cross dogs and barked in his excitement—he had found his own master!

Pierre had fallen upon his face. But Cap soon pushed him over upon his back. The sharp barking of the dog aroused the soldier, who, gazing upward, looked into the eyes of his faithful friend. "Cap—oh, Cap," gasped Pierre. "Good dog, did you come for me? Too late now, Cap," and Pierre groaned as he closed his eyes.

Cap began to lick Pierre's face with his tongue, as much as to say, "You must keep awake and I will help you." Pierre opened his eyes and looked again at Cap. Then, seeing the flask carried in the harness of the dog, he seized it eagerly and, taking a drink, he said, "You are right, Cap, I will brace up until you bring someone to help me."

The dog took the young soldier's cap between his teeth and ran back to the hospital tent. As he put the hat down, he barked again, sharply, as much as to say, "Do come quickly!"

"Now, Cap, none of that," said the doctor. "We will go to your soldier, but you must not command us."

Soon the ambulance men followed the excited dog to the young soldier, who had fainted again. Cap began to lick Pierre's hands and to kiss his face.

"Here, Cap, down," said the young doctor. "You must not be rough with your caresses."

But the wounded soldier boy opened his eyes, and said, "My dog—good dog—Cap—saved my life, when I went for a lost lamb, once—Now, again—just in time— good dog—Cap."

Cap walked slowly behind the ambulance that carried his master to the hospital, where he stretched out by the door, waiting and watching. All night long he watched and waited; he would not go out in the field again, for his own master might need him.

The doctor, who understood dogs as well as men, would not let them order the dog away. "Look at his big eyes. He is suffering with his young master. No, Cap shall stay here and watch. The other dogs can do the field work." He took off the harness from Cap and let him stay on guard at the door.

Cap watched for several days and nights, and every time the door opened he would look anxiously at the doctor. "All right, Cap, your master will pull through," said the doctor at last.

Sure enough, that day Pierre opened his eyes to the world again. His delirium had passed. He asked for Cap and the dog was brought in. With his paws resting on his master's cot, Cap looked lovingly into his face.

"You saved my life, Cap, and when I am well and strong I will go back into the trenches. We must both fight for France, you and I, and now, old Cap, you must go back to the field and look after the wounded. I shall be all right again and will do my part, but Cap, you must go back now. Good-bye, good dog, Cap!"

Cap gave his head a shake and then, looking earnestly at his young master, he licked Pierre's face and hands. After this good-bye caress, he trotted out and stood at attention before the doctor.

The doctor understood and buckled on Cap's Red Cross uniform and fitted him out for field work again. Then he bent over the dog and, patting him upon his head, he said the very words of the young master: "Good-bye, Cap; good dog, Cap!"

---

delirium—*mental confusion*

Character Theme—Loyalty/Service
& Friendship

Time to Think

1. Where did Cap get his name?
2. How had Cap saved Pierre when the boy was young?
3. How did Cap signal that he had found a wounded soldier who was alive and in need?
4. What was Cap's reaction when he found Pierre lying wounded but alive?
5. How did the doctor show that he understood Cap's anxiety for Pierre?
6. What was Cap's signal that he was ready to go back to work?

• •

WORK

Louisa May Alcott

I am glad a task to me is given
    To labor day by day;
For it brings me health, and strength, and hope,
    And I cheerfully learn to say,
"Head, you may think; Heart, you may feel,
    But Hand, you should work always."

Will Rogers was a very well known and popular American who made people laugh with his easygoing ways and witty stories. He was born on a ranch near Oologah in the Indian Territory (now Oklahoma). Because he was part Cherokee Indian, he used to say, "My ancestors may not have come over on the *Mayflower*, but they met 'em at the boat." Will Rogers died in a plane crash in 1935. Perhaps this story will make you feel as if you knew him.

Will Rogers—
The Cherokee Kid

Guernsey Van Riper, Jr.

Three newspaper reporters were waiting in the White House in Washington, D.C., to see the President.

"What's holding us up?" asked a reporter.

"Someone's flying into town to see Mr. Hoover," said another. "He's to go in ahead of us. Must be a very important person."

The door opened. "The President will see you now," a secretary said to someone.

All three reporters looked up with interest, wanting to know who it was that could get right in to see the President.

They were surprised at the appearance of the man. He was wearing a rumpled blue suit and carrying a battered old hat. His eyes were bright and twinkling under a mass of unruly hair. As he walked through the door, he pushed back a long lock which hung over his forehead.

"Who in the world is that?" asked the young newsman. "How does he get in to see the President? He doesn't look like much of anybody."

"You mean you don't recognize him?" asked the third reporter, an older man. He laughed loudly and slapped his knee. "And you call yourself a reporter! Why, millions of people wouldn't start the day without reading what *he* writes for the papers. He's our greatest humorist since Mark Twain. That's Will Rogers!"

The young reporter was embarrassed. "Well, I never saw him before," he said. "I've heard he never puts on any airs, but—"

"But you are still surprised—at the way he looks—that old blue suit, maybe?"

The young reporter nodded. "That's right. I guess that's what fooled me."

"I'll bet that's the same suit he wore to dinner with the Prince of Wales!" said the older man. "He's met the most important people in the world, and I'll bet he hasn't dressed up once."

"You know, I've often wondered," said the young man, "why Will Rogers is so popular. What has he done that everyone loves him so? And I wonder what he's doing here."

"Young man," said the older reporter, "I could talk for two weeks and not begin to tell you all the things that man's done in his life."

"Didn't he start out as a cowboy?" asked the second reporter.

"He did. And I think he'd still rather be that than anything. Let's see, now. You might say he's an entertainer, a humorist, and an actor. He's a writer and a reporter. You could also say he's one of the most generous people who ever lived—and has more common sense than most of the people in the country put together."

"How did he ever get started on a career like that?" the young reporter asked. He still could hardly believe that the plain, pleasant-looking man he had seen was the famous Will Rogers.

"Well, I know this much," said the older man. "After he left school he hired out as a cowboy in Texas and the Southwest. Then he sold some cattle and started out to see the world. South America first. Then he caught on with a show in South Africa. Did rope tricks. They called him the Cherokee Kid. Then he went to Australia, and came back again to the United States."

"That's covering a lot of territory."

"Why, he was still just a kid," said the older man. "Then he got into rodeos and Wild West shows and ended up in New York. He was on the stage there for years. He made a great hit."

"You mean, just roping and riding tricks?"

"At first, yes. Like all Americans, Will wanted to be the best there is—at something. He worked until he was the best trick roper in the world. That was only the beginning, though!"

"How do you mean?"

"Why, that just gave him a bigger opportunity! He used to talk to himself on the stage. One day the audience heard him. They were so amused that he started talking with his act all the time—and he's been talking ever since."

"Did you hear him on the radio last year?" asked the second reporter. "He just talks about the important things that are going on in the world—and what he says makes sense. He puts it in a humorous way; when people laugh they don't forget so easily what he has said."

"You've got it right!" said the older man. "There are lots of good comedians and actors, but there is only one Will Rogers. Somehow, he stands for the best in America. He's made a great success, yet he's friendly and modest, and always ready to help the other fellow."

"You know what he was paid for those radio talks?" said the second reporter. "Some tremendous sum—the most ever paid. And do you know what he did with it? He gave it all to charity."

"You know," said the older reporter, "there's something he said once that tells more about him than anything else. He has made many famous remarks, but this is my favorite Will Rogers saying—'I never met a man I didn't like.'"

All three were silent for a minute.

"I suppose that's the answer," said the second reporter. "He really loves people. I've heard him scold a lot of people when he gets talking about politics, though."

"Certainly," said the older man. "He can see faults and spot a faker quicker than anyone. He can take down someone who's got a swelled head, but that doesn't mean he doesn't like them. He's never mean about his scoldings—he always does it in a kindly way—a humorous way."

"I wonder what he's doing here today."

"I expect it's got something to do with the drought and hard times."

"When people are in trouble you can always expect Will Rogers to be interested," said the older reporter. "And now especially, when Oklahoma has poor crops and everyone is so hungry. You know, Will always says he comes from Claremore, Oklahoma—even though he lives in California."

The door opened. Will Rogers was saying good-bye to President Herbert Hoover.

When he turned to leave, all three newspapermen jumped up to ask him questions.

Will gave them a broad, good-natured grin.

"Mr. Rogers, could we have a statement—about your talk with the President?" asked one.

"Well, boys, looks as though you got me corralled," said Will. "Now I haven't much to say. The President and I have been having a talk about hungry people. Looks serious."

"Is the government going to put up money to help?" asked the second reporter.

"Mr. Hoover sincerely feels it would be the wrong thing for the government to give money to the Red Cross," said Will. He pursed his lips and looked droll. "Course, everybody in Washington wants to feed hungry people— but everyone wants to do it his own way."

The reporters chuckled. One of them asked, "What do you think ought to be done?"

"Now, all I know is what I read in the papers," said Will, "so I'm going to Oklahoma to see for myself. I'm going to try to raise some money for the Red Cross, too, to help those people."

"I thought you had something up your sleeve, or you wouldn't be joking about it."

"Well, I figure a man who can't laugh a little when the going is tough just doesn't know how to live."

"What are you planning—a series of shows? Roping and stunts and talks?"

"I figured the Navy would lend me an airplane, so my friend Captain Frank Hawks and I could barnstorm around and talk to folks."

All the newsmen knew the famous Captain Frank Hawks, who held the transcontinental speed record for airplanes.

"When do you start?" asked the older one.

"Well, I'll have to line up a few entertainers—say a quartet and accordionist and trick roper."

"What are they for?"

Will cocked his head on one side. "Got to have somebody along to take the folks' minds off me. How else can we fool 'em into giving money? You see, when I get down to Oklahoma, it'll be the first time I've done my act there. I'm afraid they aren't going to be much impressed. They'll say, 'Why, that's just old Will, talkin' as he used to on the street corner. And that rope twirlin'—why, any old cowboy could do that!' "

Everyone laughed.

---

barnstorm—*to travel around making speeches*

"I reckon you boys'll pardon me. I'd better go 'long and see about my arrangements."

Will Rogers nodded to the reporters and hurried away. For a moment no one said anything. Then the older newsman said, "Did you ever see anyone so modest? Why, the people will come from all over the Southwest to hear him talk and watch him throw his rope."

"I'd like to be there," said the young reporter. "Somehow, just talking to him makes you feel good. Makes you forget your troubles."

So it happened that on February 13 the airport at Texarkana, on the border of Texas and Arkansas, was crowded. People were rushing up to the fence watching for a plane to come in.

"There she is!" said a tall man near the gate.

A speedy biplane circled the field and settled down to a perfect landing.

"That's the fastest plane the Navy owns," said the tall fellow to the man next to him. "The government loaned it to Will Rogers just for this trip. I don't know anyone else they'd do that for."

The plane taxied up to the gate and out stepped Will Rogers. He grinned and nodded to the people crowding around while everyone cheered.

"I'm not the fellow you want," said Will. "Here he is, Captain Frank Hawks, the famous pilot." As he hurried Captain Hawks out of the plane, Captain Hawks laughed and shook his head. Everyone joined in the laughter. Yes, they were interested in Captain Hawks, but it was Will Rogers they had come to see.

---

biplane—*an airplane with two pairs of wings, one above the other*

Will and Captain Hawks pushed through the crowd, got into a car, and were driven away.

The tall man called to his companion, "Let's hurry down to the auditorium. He's going to make a speech right away; maybe we can get in."

The two men jumped into their car. There was so much traffic they had to wait.

"This is the fiftieth city Will Rogers has visited in just three weeks," said the tall man. "Sometimes he's made six speeches a day. How can he do it?"

"I read in the paper that he's raised two hundred and twenty-five thousand dollars to help the people who are hungry and out of work," said his companion, "and he gave five thousand dollars himself in each of the three states he has visited—Texas, Oklahoma, and Arkansas. What do you think of that?"

The tall man nodded wisely. "It's wonderful."

They parked as near the auditorium as they could. When they reached the doors, they couldn't get in—the hall was full. People had come from all around the countryside to see and hear Will Rogers—and to help him raise money for the needy.

The tall man pushed his way up to the door. "Maybe we can stand in the back."

As he opened the door, the crowd inside roared with laughter at something Will Rogers had said. On the stage Will was sitting on the edge of a table, twirling a rope.

When the laughter died down, Will said to the audience, "You're doing fine. We'll get out early today. It takes just twice as long to get out when I have to explain the jokes."

The crowd laughed again.

The usher moved up to the tall man. "Sorry, no room for anyone else," he whispered.

The two men went outside again.

The tall fellow said, "A lot of important people think Will ought to run for President. He'd be good, too. He's a great man."

His companion said, "Yes, I know. Will won't listen to it, though. He says he ought to go right on doing what he knows best. He thinks he can do more for people that way."

Character Theme—Compassion/Charity
& Resourcefulness

Time to Think

1. Why did the reporter say about Will, "He doesn't look like much of anybody"?
2. Was Will Rogers a writer, entertainer, actor, cowboy, reporter, or comedian?
3. Why were Will and Captain Hawks barnstorming?
4. Why do you think the politicians didn't get angry when Will scolded them?
5. What made Will Rogers so popular?

No Sense in Pretense

Author Unknown

You tell what you are by the friends you seek,
By the manner in which you speak.
By the way you employ your leisure time,
By the use you make of dollar and dime.
You tell what you are by the things you wear,
By the spirit in which you burdens bear,
By the sense of humor that you display
By the music that your stereo plays
You tell what you are by the way you walk,
By the things of which you delight to talk,
By the manner in which you bear defeat,
By so simple a thing as how you eat.
By the books you choose from the well-filled shelf;
In these ways and more, you tell on yourself.
So there's really no particle of sense
In any effort at pretense.

---

pretense—*false behavior or appearance*

A FAILURE?

Author Unknown

When Abraham Lincoln was a young man, he ran for the legislature in Illinois and was badly swamped.

He next entered business, failed, spent seventeen years of his life paying up the debts of a worthless partner.

He was in love with a beautiful young woman to whom he became engaged—then she died.

Entering politics again, he ran for Congress and again was badly defeated.

He then tried to get an appointment to the United States Land Office, but he failed.

He became a candidate for the U.S. Senate, and was badly defeated.

In 1856 he became a candidate for the Vice Presidency and was again defeated.

In 1858 he was defeated by Douglas.

One failure after another—bad failures—great setbacks. In the face of all this he eventually became one of the country's greatest men, if not the greatest.

When you think of a series of setbacks like this, doesn't it make you feel kind of small to become discouraged, just because you think you are having a hard time in life?

Henry Ford: Dreamer on Wheels

Dorothy Haas

The inside of the little brick shed was lighted by a flickering kerosene lamp. In its dim light a man worked over a machine—part bicycle, part carriage, part engine. The man's face was pale and tired. Great, dark shadows showed under his eyes.

"Henry Ford!"

The voice came from the doorway. The man looked up. His wife stood there. Her nightdress and slippers showed underneath the fringed shawl she had wrapped around her. Rain dotted the big black umbrella she carried.

"Henry," she said, "it's two o'clock in the morning! You simply must get some rest tonight, or you'll—"

"Clara," her husband said mildly, "you'll catch cold, out here in the night air." He grinned at her. "But I'm glad you came, anyway. Look, here!"

As his wife moved closer, he reached into the engine.

"We fasten this," he said, "to—this. And—we tighten—this nut—a bit more, and"—he picked up an old rag and wiped his hands—"we are ready to try this horseless carriage, this 'quadricycle'!"

Clara Ford forgot the lateness of the hour. "Do you mean to say it's ready to test right now—this minute?" she said, her eyes round.

Henry grinned at her. "Right now," he said. "There couldn't be a better time. There won't be any horses on the street to be scared by the noise. And anyway, I

---

kerosene—*a thin oil used as fuel*
quadricycle—*a light, open vehicle mounted on four wheels*

just can't wait until tomorrow!"

He pushed the automobile—for an automobile it was—out of the shed. He started the engine.

"If this thing works right tonight, I'll give you the second ride in it tomorrow. That is," he called back over his shoulder, "if you have a cup of good hot chocolate ready for me when I get back."

Clara waved after him. "It will work right," she called. "I'll have the second ride in it. Your chocolate will be waiting, Henry."

Henry turned out of the alley. He drove down Bagley to Grand River Avenue. From there he turned onto Washington Boulevard.

He had to be careful. The streets were dark. The paving bricks did not always fit tightly together—where there were paving bricks! Some of the streets were unpaved. The ruts were slippery in the rain.

He took a deep breath of the misty, warm air and smiled to himself. His gasoline-engine-driven carriage worked just fine.

It was a bit noisy, of course. He looked up at the silent, dark houses. The noise didn't seem bad enough to wake anyone, though. Detroiters certainly were sound sleepers!

Satisfied, he turned his little automobile and headed back toward Number 58 Bagley Avenue, toward his cup of hot chocolate and a few hours of much-needed sleep.

The months that followed were busy ones. During the day he worked at his job as engineer at the Edison Illuminating Company. At night he worked in the little shed on Bagley Avenue.

The horseless carriage, the "quadricycle," became an everyday sight around Detroit. At the sound of its sputtering, chugging engine on the street, people ran out of houses and stores. They lined up on the sidewalks to watch it pass.

Drivers of carriages had to hold a tight rein on their horses. The animals were terrified by this noisy, smelly beast that raced past them at speeds up to twenty miles an hour.

The men with whom he worked knew of Henry's experiments. Some of them thought he was wasting his time.

"Where could you ever get enough gasoline to drive the thing?" they said. "Now, with a horse—why, you just turn it out in the nearest pasture!"

Other men thought he had an interesting invention. Few of them went so far, though, as to say it had a future. "Who ever could build enough of them to go around," they said, "even if people did want to buy them!"

In August of that same year, 1896, four men from the Edison Company were chosen to go to New York. A big meeting was being held there for Edison men from many parts of the country. Henry was one of the men chosen to go to the meeting.

The meeting went on for several days. On the last day a dinner was held. Present at the dinner was the master inventor himself—Thomas Edison, the Wizard of Menlo Park!

During the meal, talk turned to cars that were then being built. Some cars ran on the principle of the steam engine. Their fires had to be fed. Water in boilers created steam, which made the cars run.

Other cars were run by electric batteries. These were silent and smooth running. But, since batteries go dead, they could not travel far from electrical charging stations.

"Mr. Edison," said one of the men from Detroit, "this young man"—he pointed at Henry—"has built a gasoline-engine-driven carriage. He drives it around Detroit, scaring all our horses half to death!"

Thomas Edison turned and looked at Henry. "You don't say!" he said. Here was a young man who worked for his company, an electric power company—and yet who built a gasoline-powered carriage!

Henry felt his face grow red. Would Mr. Edison be angry?

Thomas Edison wasn't angry. He smiled. "Here, young fellow," he said. "Sit next to me. I want to hear about this invention of yours."

Henry moved into the seat next to Mr. Edison. He swallowed. But then he forgot to be nervous as he began to talk on his favorite subject.

"You know how a gasoline engine works, sir," he said. "Mine has two cylinders. Power goes from the engine to the wheels by a system of belts and chains."

He went on to explain the workings of his invention. "The car carries its own fuel," he said. "A tank under the seat holds three gallons of gasoline. Altogether, it's a light motor, meant to drive a light carriage. It *has* to be light," he added with a smile, "to run on our rutted dirt roads!"

Talk at the table had stopped. Everybody was listening to the young fellow from Detroit. Most interested of all was Thomas Edison.

Henry finished. "That's about it, sir," he said. "If you ever come out to Detroit, I'll be happy to give you a ride in it."

Thomas Edison dropped his fist to the table so hard that the china rattled. "That's it!" he exclaimed. "That's the kind of mechanical carriage we need!

"It doesn't need an engineer and a fireman to run it, like the steam-driven carriage. It doesn't need to stay near a power station, like the electric carriage. Young man," he said, "you're working on the kind of thing that may someday replace the horse and carriage. Just keep at it!"

Henry left the meeting and took his train back to Detroit. He didn't join in the talk of the three other men. He looked out of the window and listened to the sound of the wheels on the track. "Just-keep-at-it! Just-keep-at-it! Just-keep-at-it!" they seemed to be saying.

---

cylinders—*the chambers in an engine that produce the power*   rutted—*full of dents and holes*

And keep at it he did. He kept at it until the Ford automobile became one of the most familiar pieces of machinery on the North American continent!

Character Theme—Initiative/Resourcefulness
& Determination

Time to Think

1. What did Ford call his horseless carriage?
2. Why did Ford test his invention at two o'clock in the morning?
3. What was Ford's automobile powered by?
4. What famous inventor was impressed with Ford's invention?
5. What good advice did Edison give Ford that you can apply in your life?

The Iron Stove
of Benjamin Franklin

Carolyn Sherwin Bailey

"Did you see him today?" asked a little girl in gray, all excitement, as she opened the door to admit her brother.

The boy, shaking with the cold—for it was winter and his jacket was none too thick—set down his basket on the rough deal table, and leaned over the tiny fire that burned on the hearth. His eyes shone, though, as he turned to answer his sister.

"Yes, Beth, I saw him down at the wharf and he gave me this." As he spoke, William drew from underneath his coat, where he had tucked it to surprise Beth, a crude little brush made of rushes bound together with narrow strips of willow.

---

deal table—*a table made of fir or pine boards*

rushes—*stiff plants that grow in marshy areas*
willow—*a type of lightweight wood*

"What is it?" Beth took the brush in her hands and held it up to the light, looking at it curiously. She made a quaint picture in the shifting light of the fire, a little Quaker girl of old Philadelphia, her yellow curls tucked inside a close-fitting gray cap, and her straight gray frock reaching almost to the heels of her heavy shoes.

"It is something new for cleaning," William explained. He took the brush and began sweeping up the ashes on the hearth, as Beth watched him curiously. "Mr. Franklin brought a whole bunch of them down to the wharf to show to people, and he gave me one."

"How did he make it?" Beth asked curiously.

"It took him a whole year, for it had to grow first," William explained. "He saw some brush baskets last year that the sea captains had brought fruit in, lying in the wet on the wharf. They had sprouted and sent out shoots, so what did Mr. Franklin do but plant the shoots in his garden. They grew and this year he has a fine crop of broom corn, as he calls it. He dried it and bound it into these brushes. He has some with long handles and he calls them brooms."

The children's mother had come in from the next room and she grasped the hearth brush with eagerness.

"It is just what Philadelphia, the city of cleanliness, needs," she said as she went to work brushing the corners of the window sills and the mantel piece.

As her mother finished speaking, Beth emptied the basket that William had brought in. There was not a great deal in it—a little flour, some tea, a very tiny package of sugar, and some potatoes. She arranged them on

frock—*a dress*

the shelves in the kitchen, shivering a little as she moved about the cold room.

Chill comfort it would seem to a child today. Philadelphia was a new city, and these settlers from across the sea had brought little with them to make their lives cheerful. Outside, huge piles of snow drifted the narrow streets and were banked on the low stone doorsteps of the small red-brick houses. A chill wind blew up from the wharves and such of the Friends as were out hurried along with bent heads against which the cold beat, and they wrapped their long cloaks closely about them.

It was almost as cold in the Arnold's house as it was outside. The children's father had not been able to stand the hardships of the new country, and Beth, and William, and their mother were left to face this winter alone. Mrs. Arnold did fine sewing, and William ran errands for the sailors and merchantmen down at the wharves, having his basket filled in return for his work.

Mrs. Arnold drew her chair up to the fireplace and opened her bag of sewing. Beth leaned over her shoulder as she watched the thin, white fingers.

"Your fingers are stiff with the cold," Beth exclaimed as she blew the coals with the bellows and then rubbed her mother's hands.

"Not very," she tried to smile.

"Yes, very," William said as he swung his arms and blew on his finger tips. "We're all of us cold. It would be easier to work if we could only keep warm."

Just then he heard a rap at the brass knocker of their door. Both ran to open it, and both children shouted with

Friends—*Quakers*

234

delight as a slightly stooping figure entered. His long white hair made him look like some old patriarch. His forehead was high, and his eyes deep set in his long, thin face. He reached out two toil-hardened hands to greet the family.

"Mr. Franklin!" their mother exclaimed. "We are most glad to see you. You are our very welcome guest always, but it is very poor hospitality we are able to offer you. Our fire is very small and the house cold."

"A small fire is better than none," their guest said, "and the welcome in Friend Arnold's house is always so warm that it makes a fire unnecessary. Still," he looked at the children's blue lips and pinched cheeks, "I wish that your hearth were wider."

He crossed to the fireplace, feeling of the bricks and measuring with his eye the breadth and depth of the opening in the chimney. He seemed lost in thought for a moment, and then his face suddenly shone with a smile like the one it had worn when he had seen the first green shoots of the broom corn pushing their way up through the ground of his garden.

"What is it, Mr. Franklin?" Beth asked. "What do you see up in our chimney?"

"A surprise," the good neighbor of Philadelphia replied. "If I make no mistake in my plans, you will see that surprise before long. In the meantime, be of good cheer."

He was gone as quickly as he had come, but he had left a glow of cheer and neighborliness behind him. All Philadelphia was warmed in this way by Benjamin Franklin. Whenever he crossed a threshold, he brought the spirit of comfort and helpfulness to the house.

---

patriarch—*a recognized ruler or leader of a group*   breadth—*width*

"What do you suppose he meant?" Beth asked as the door closed behind the quaint figure of the man.

"I wonder," said William. Then he took out his speller and copy book and the words of their visitor were soon forgotten.

But all Philadelphia began to wonder soon at the doings at the big white house where Benjamin Franklin lived. The neighbors were used to hearing busy sounds of hammering and tinkering coming from the back where Franklin had built a workshop. Now, however, he sent away for a small forge and its flying sparks could be seen and the sound of its bellows heard in the stillness of the long, cold winter nights. Great slabs of iron were unloaded for him at the wharf, and for days no one saw him. He was shut up in his workshop and from morning until night passers-by heard ringing blows on iron coming from it as if it were the shop of some country blacksmith.

In the middle of the winter Beth and William and their mother went to a friend's house to stay for a week. Mrs. Arnold was not well, and the house was very cold. The week for which they were invited lengthened into two, then three.

"We must go home," Mrs. Arnold said at last. "Mr. Franklin said that he would stop this afternoon and help William carry the carpetbag. It is time that we began our work again."

As they took their homeward way through the snow, they noticed, again, the happy smile on Mr. Franklin's face. He held the handle of the bag with one hand and Beth's chilly fingers with the other. He was the spryest

---

forge—*a furnace where metals are heated*　　　　spryest—*liveliest*
carpetbag—*suitcase made of carpet fabric*

of them all as he hurried along. They understood why, as they opened the door of their home.

They started, at first, wondering if by any chance they had come to the wrong house. No, there were the familiar things just as they had left them; the row of shining copper pans on the wall, the polished candlesticks on the mantel-piece, the warming pan in the corner, and the braided rugs on the floor. But the house was as warm as summer. They had never felt such comfortable heat in the winter before. In the fireplace, that had been all too tiny, against the chimney, was a crude iron stove, partly like a fireplace in shape, but with a top and sides that held and spread the heat of the fire inside until the whole room glowed with it.

"That is my surprise," Mr. Franklin explained, rubbing his hands with pleasure as he saw the wonder and delight in the faces of the others, "an iron wonder to drive out the cold and frighten away the frosts. You can cook on it,

or hang the kettle over the coals. It will keep the coals alive all night and not eat up as much coal as your drafty fireplace did. This is my winter gift to my dear Friend Arnolds."

"Oh, how wonderful! How can we thank you for it? We, who were so poor, are the richest family in all Philadelphia now. How I shall be able to work!" the children's mother said.

Beth and William put out their hands to catch the friendly warmth from this, the first stove in the City of Friends. It warmed them through and through. Then William examined its rough mechanism so that he would be able to tend it, and Beth bustled about the room, filling the shining brass teakettle and putting a teaspoonful of tea in the pot to draw a cup for her mother and Mr. Franklin. At last she turned to him, her blue eyes looking deep into his.

"You are so good to us," Beth said. "Why did you work so hard to invent this iron stove for us?"

The kindest friend that old Philadelphia ever had stopped a second to think. He never knew the reasons for his good deeds. They were as natural as the flowering of the broom corn in his garden. At last he spoke:

"Because of your warm hearts, little Friend," he said. "Not that they needed any more heat, but that you may see their glow reflected in the fires you kindle in my stove."

And so we may feel the kindly warmth of Benjamin Franklin's heart in our stoves, which are so much better, but all modeled after the one he made for his neighbors in the Quaker City of long ago.

Character Theme—Thoughtfulness
& Friendship

Time to Think

1. Was the Arnold family rich or poor? How do you know?
2. What did Mrs. Arnold do to earn money?
3. What was Mr. Franklin's surprise for the Arnold family?
4. Why did Mr. Franklin build the stove for his friends?
5. How do we benefit even today from Franklin's invention?

Bell of Liberty

Peter Faneuil

There was tumult in the city,
　In the quaint old Quaker town,
And the streets were rife with people
　Pacing restless up and down;
People gathering at corners,
　Where they whispered each to each,
And the sweat stood on their temples,
　With the earnestness of speech.

As the black Atlantic currents
　Lash the wild Newfoundland shore,
So they beat against the State House,
　So they surged against the door;
And the mingling of their voices
　Made a harmony profound,
Till the quiet street of Chestnut
　Was all turbulent with sound.

---

tumult—*the noise of a crowd*　　　**rife**—*abundant*

"Will they do it?"   "Dare they do it?"

  "Who is speaking?"   "What's the news?"

"What of Adams?"   "What of Sherman?"

  "O, God, grant they won't refuse!"

"Make some way, there!"   "Let me nearer!"

  "I am stifling!"—"Stifle then:

When a nation's life's at hazard,

  We've no time to think of men!"

So they beat against the portal—

  Man and woman, maid and child;

And the July sun in Heaven

  On the scene looked down and smiled;

The same sun that saw the Spartan

  Shed his patriot blood in vain,

Now beheld the soul of freedom

  All unconquered rise again.

Aloft in that high steeple

  Sat the bellman, old and gray;

He was weary of the tyrant

  And his iron-sceptered sway;

So he sat with one hand ready

  On the clapper of the bell,

When his eye should catch the signal,

  The long expected news to tell.

See! see! the dense crowd quivers

  Through all its lengthy line,

As the boy beside the portal

  Looks forth to give the sign!

With his small hands upward lifted,

  Breezes dallying with his hair,

Hark! with deep, clear intonation,

  Breaks his young voice on the air.

---

stifling—*suffocating*   **Spartan**—*a courageous soldier*
hazard—*a dangerous place*   **intonation**—*the tone of one's voice*
portal—*doorway*

Hushed the people's swelling murmur,
  List the boy's strong joyous cry!
"Ring!" he shouts aloud; "RING! Grandpa!
  Ring! O, RING for LIBERTY!"
And straightway, at the signal,
  The old bellman lifts his hand,
And sends the good news, making
  Iron music through the land.

How they shouted! What rejoicing!
  How the old bell shook the air,
Till the clang of freedom ruffled
  The calmly gliding Delaware!
How the bonfires and the torches
  Lighted up the night's repose,
And from the flames, like Phoenix,
  Fair liberty arose!

That old State House bell is silent—
  Hushed is now its clamorous tongue;
But the spirit it awakened
  Still is living—ever young.
And when we greet the sunlight
  On the Fourth of each July,
We will ne'er forget the bellman,
  Who, betwixt the earth and sky,
Rang out our Independence,
  Which, please God, shall never die!

Phoenix—*a mythological bird that
    burned in a fire and later came to
    life out of the ashes*
clamorous—*noisy*
betwixt—*between*

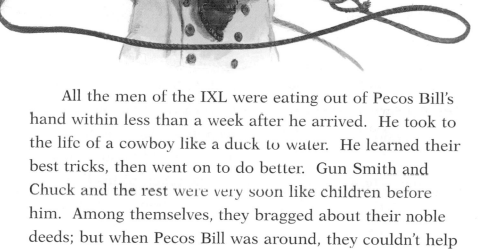

Meet Pecos Bill, the cowboy who
could lasso anything this side of China.

Pecos Bill Invents Modern Cowpunching

James Cloyd Bowman

All the men of the IXL were eating out of Pecos Bill's
hand within less than a week after he arrived. He took to
the life of a cowboy like a duck to water. He learned their
best tricks, then went on to do better. Gun Smith and
Chuck and the rest were very soon like children before
him. Among themselves, they bragged about their noble
deeds; but when Pecos Bill was around, they couldn't help
thinking that they were merely bridled cayuses.

He could stand on the ground beside a bronco, turn
an air flop, and land astride the pony before it had time
to tighten a muscle. He could ride bareback with no
bridle. He could urge his pony at top speed over ground

Pecos (pā′kōs)   *cayuse—a horse*

243

so rough and uneven that Gun Smith and the others were afraid even to attempt it with bit and saddle. And since he was so casual and modest about everything he did, they thought Pecos the eighth wonder of the world. Almost at once he was full of ideas. And what ideas!

Up to Pecos Bill's day, when a man wanted to capture a horse or a steer, he would lay a piece of rope down on the ground, make a loop in one end of it, sit down behind a tree or a blind, and by laying a bait, try to coax the wild critter to step within the loop. He would then jerk sharply on the rope, and perhaps one time in a dozen, if he was lucky, he would succeed in making a catch. It was no uncommon thing for a man to wait around and lose an entire month's time without laying hold of so much as a single animal.

"Well, this sort of thing has got to be changed," said Pecos Bill to himself when no one else was near to hear him. "A man can't be expected to waste his entire lifetime catching a single horse or cow."

Without further delay, Pecos got hold of the longest piece of rope he could find around the ranch, and began to throw it through the air. Next he rode off alone where the others could not see what he was doing. After three days of constant practice, he found that he could lasso almost anything. He was limited only by the reach of his line.

Pecos Bill would just make a large loop in one end of his rope, swing it wildly about his head three or four times, and then, with a quick flip of his forearm and wrist, send it flying like a bullet. As he became more and more skilled, he added rapidly to the length of his rope.

As soon as he was entirely sure of himself, Pecos asked the boys to come out and let him show them his new invention.

244

"See that roan steer across there? That's Old Crook-horn, our wildest critter, ain't it?" Pecos asked the boys quietly.

Before anyone was aware of what he was doing, Pecos Bill had whirled his loop about his head and had sent it so fast in the direction of the four-year-old that the eye could scarcely follow it.

In an instant the old steer began to jump and bellow, and Pecos Bill began to tow in the rope. Soon the astonished steer stood with lowered head before the even more surprised cowboys.

Not content with this great skill, Pecos began practicing from horseback.

In another week, he again called his cowboys out to see what he could do. They watched him with popping eyes, as he gave his rope a double turn around his saddlebow. He then started his bronco at a hard gallop. They saw him quickly approach a rather tall, scraggly

roan—*reddish brown or chestnut with white spots*

mesquite tree, whirl his loop wildly about his head, and then fling it into the air. When he dragged a great hawk down from the topmost branch with the noose about its neck, the men were unable to believe their eyes.

"What sort o' wonder worker is this, anyway?" they asked each other. "No human could ever throw the rope like that!"

Then Pecos Bill showed the men how it was done, and after two or three months of hard practice, each of them was able to make frequent catches with his own lariat at a distance of from ten to not more than twenty feet.

In the meantime, Pecos Bill had become dissatisfied with the fact that he couldn't find a longer rope. So he began to braid himself a cowhide lariat. This is how he went to work. First he looked up some old horned steers that had lived so many years within the depths of the trees that there were green algae on their backs—mossbacks, sure enough. What's more, these steers were so old their faces were gray and wrinkled.

Whenever Pecos Bill got hold of one of these old fellows, he first loosened the hide behind the ears. He then grasped the steer by the tail, and, with a flip of his wrist and forearm and a wild yowl, he frightened the animal so that it jumped out of its skin. The tough hides of these old mossbacks were just what Pecos needed.

Three or four years later, when he had it finished, his loyal ranchers declared on all sides that the lariat was as long as the equator, and that Pecos could lasso anything this side of China.

---

mesquite—*a small shrub that grows in desert regions*

It was thus that Pecos Bill solved one of the problems that had worried cowhands and their bosses for years.

Pecos Bill began looking around to find other worlds to conquer. He instructed the men how to live in the saddle, and how to take cat naps astride their grazing ponies. He showed them, too, how to soothe the cattle by crooning songs to them, and how to keep the herd together without annoying even the leaders.

When the herd stampeded, as it was sure to do at times, Pecos taught the men how to turn the leaders, and thus start the entire herd milling in a circle until the cattle finally winded themselves, and stopped through sheer weariness in the very spot from which they had started in the first place.

During these days, Cooky was the busiest man this side of Mars. After trying for a week to feed the men by carrying food out to them from the ranch shack, he finally gave up. On four or five different occasions, as he was starting out with his kettles and pans, he actually met himself on the trail coming back with the empty dishes of the previous afternoon. If he hadn't stopped his foolishness of trying to work twenty-seven hours a day just when he did, most likely his ghost would still be wandering on the wind over the same trails.

In the despair of complete exhaustion, Cooky finally hitched two spans of mules to the chuck wagon, loaded it down with enough food to last a fortnight, and left the ranch shack to take care of itself. He hadn't been gone half an hour before the place looked as deserted as the ruins of Pompeii.

---

crooning—*singing softly*
fortnight—*two weeks*

Pompeii—*an Italian city that was destroyed by a volcano*

Very soon the entire life of the ranch was clicking like clockwork and Pecos Bill was so pleased, for the present at least, that he couldn't think of anything left to invent. So he decided to go out and tell the world about what he had been doing, not for the sake of his own fame, but only for the benefit of the cowmen of the entire range country.

One evening, after the cattle had settled down for the first sleep of the night, Pecos Bill announced to Gun Smith, his foreman, that it would be necessary for him to go away from the ranch for a few days. "If anybody asks where I am," he whispered, "just tell them that I'll be back for breakfast, like as not."

Pecos then took his boots under his arm, threw his coiled rope over his shoulder, and went bounding off across the rolling prairie. When he came to a strange ranch, he would quickly put on his boots and walk in great dignity, with jangling spurs, up to the boss of the outfit. Very soon he would be telling the wide-eyed cowman his story. In this way he easily covered forty or fifty miles in an hour and a half or two hours.

Pecos Bill thus visited all the ranches of the entire Southwest within two or three months. Not forgetting a single detail, he told the men everywhere what he had done. At first they thought him the biggest liar that had ever been invented in the whole world of cowmen. But when he had limbered up his lariat, and when they had witnessed his performance, they were quite willing to believe everything he told them.

What they saw was even more wonderful than what he had said. For with perfect ease, he would lasso any animal within reach of their vision. Pecos could lasso a grazing or a galloping steer, or lay his flying noose around the neck of a bald eagle in full flight.

The flying visits led later to many heated disputes among the puzzled ranchers: "You say this Pecos Bill left Hub's Ferry at nine o'clock? But he was at Slippery Mike's by eleven, and that's a good forty miles as the crow flies, ain't it? And he was alone and on foot, wasn't he? Who is this Pecos Bill, anyway?" Every rancher seemed to have a bigger yarn to tell than the one that his neighbor had.

But they were all true—certainly! And through the efforts of Pecos Bill, ranchmen began to have a spring roundup and a fall roundup. Pecos persuaded the ranchers of a given range section or river valley to drive together all the cattle of the entire district. They then sorted them into individual herds according to the particular brand of each owner. After his work was completed, each owner branded all of his calves. The strays, with no brand, and the orphan mavericks were then distributed equally and branded so that they could never again go astray. And every bit of the plan was Pecos Bill's.

In the fall the roundup was repeated so that the stray cattle could be located and given back to their rightful owners. After all the exchanges were made, the cowmen, as they took their herds back to their individual feeding grounds, found it easy to count the number of steers that were in condition for the market and the number that they would have to pasture during the coming winter.

Thus it was that each owner was given what belonged to him, according to the laws of reason, and not in accordance with the earlier outlawry of the pistol.

---

mavericks—*calves that are separated from their mothers*

And so it came about very naturally, through the organization of all the scattered cowmen, that the fame of Pecos Bill rapidly spread to the four corners of the range country. From the valley of the Rio Grande, through Texas and New Mexico, Arizona and Colorado, Kansas and Nebraska, and far into the wilderness of Montana and Wyoming, cowboys, when they met, would carelessly throw one foot free from its stirrup and in a resting position shout to their nearest companion, "Say, have you heard about the rope Uncle Bill is still braidin' down on the Pecos? It's already twice as long as the equator! You know, if Old Pecos Bill could only get a toe hold on the moon, he'd turn in and lasso this wanderin' planet of ours and bring it back into the Milky Way, where it belongs! Yes, and Pecos could do it easier than you or I could lasso a year-old heifer calf!"

Character Theme—Initiative

Time to Think

1. How did Pecos Bill happen to invent lasso-throwing?
2. Where did Pecos Bill get the cowhide for the lariat?
3. What resulted from Pecos Bill's visit to other ranches?
4. Name some reasons why this story is purely imaginative.

The Fighting Red Tails: America's First Black Airmen

Warren Holliburton

This is the story of the first black American pilots and their brave exploits in World War II.

On April 1, 1943, the airmen left Tuskegee Institute in Alabama, the famous college for black students founded by Booker T. Washington, and joined the war against Hitler in Italy. Their courageous and inspiring leader was Colonel Benjamin O. Davis, Jr., the first black man to graduate from West Point in almost fifty years.

Slowly the Red Tails gained experience and victories. With the addition of three more squadrons of pilots from Tuskegee, they formed a new and larger all-black air unit— the 332nd Fighter Group. On March 31, 1944, the 332nd got a new job—escorting bombers of the 15th Air Force.

All through the month of June 1944, the 332nd flew with the bombers of the 15th Air Force. The bombing targets were in Italy, southern France, and the Balkans.

---

squadrons—*small military units*
Balkans—*Greece and countries that surround the Balkan peninsula*

It seemed that they were meeting enemy planes on every bombing run. Each battle was worse than the last, and more and more pilots of the 332nd were lost. The enemy seemed to know the Americans were losing. They fought that much harder, sending new planes to stop the Americans from knocking out their supply lines.

Just west of Aircasea, Italy, was a strip of landing ground believed to be one of the Nazi's most important air supply lines. The American army knew that Italy would fall if they could keep supplies from reaching the enemy's front lines. The job of wiping out the supply lines fell to the 332nd.

The American air attack had to be done in a special way, for if the enemy learned of it, they would be able to find the P-47 fighters almost immediately. A giant radar network along the Italian coast protected the Nazis against just such attacks. The 332nd Squadron had only one way to keep from being spotted. That was to fly low—too low to be picked up by radar. There was no doubt that the plan was dangerous, but it was the only way to get the job done.

Aircasea (âr·cŏs′ē·ə)

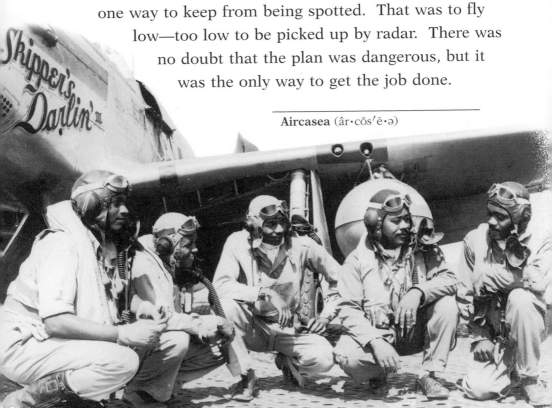

On June 24, the black fighter squadron took off, skimming low over the waters of the Mediterranean Sea. The weather was bad; thick, dark clouds blotted out the sunlight.

Suddenly, the engine of one plane cut out, and the plane dipped into the water. Pulling back on his stick, the pilot lifted his plane. But the engine failed to catch, and the P-47 nosed back down and crashed. It sank almost immediately.

Every man in the group watched in horror, but the 332nd continued on. Now and then a giant wave lashed upward toward the low-flying airplanes. Suddenly another plane slipped too low and was slapped at by the waves. When the pilot tried to pull up, he discovered that the weight of the fuel and bombs made his plane sluggish.

A wing was ripped by water. The pilot jumped out just before the plane skidded and crashed, luckily escaping the quickly sinking craft.

One of the other pilots spotted the man in the sea and went after him in a tight 180-degree turn. A downward gust of air caught his plane, throwing it into a flat spin. A moment later the plane exploded as it hit the sea. Neither pilot could be seen through the thick, heavy smoke that covered the water.

By this time the 332nd was halfway to its target—but its problems were by no means over. The lead pilot had made a mistake. He had turned east at the place where he should have turned north. Reaching the coast, the planes were more than 70 miles from where they should have been. The lead pilot saw his mistake and made a 90-degree turn.

He evidently was closer to the water than he thought because all of a sudden he saw the water rush up toward him. But it was too late. All at once the plane plunged into the waves and a moment later the giant explosion it made lifted the sea. No trace of the plane was to be seen. The radio was still. No one said a word as the assistant flight leader moved forward to take the lead.

At last the planes were close to the target. But now a thick fog began to roll in, and the pilots could not see the ground below them. As they closed in on the Nazi supply strip, the fog got thicker. Nothing could be seen of the enemy. The new flight leader made a painful decision.

"Give it up! Give up the target. We're going home!" he called into the radio.

This was a terrible blow to the pilots of the 332nd. Four good men already had lost their lives on this flight— and for nothing. The enemy had not even been touched!

The next day, the pilots of the 332nd answered the call from Flight Operations. Their hearts were heavy, but every man knew the flight had to go on. Their job this time was some low-flying bombing of roads in northern Italy, known to be the enemy's main supply lines for the fighting further south. If they were destroyed, much of the enemy's strength would be cut.

The 332nd went to work. Although no one said it, each man wanted to lash back with greater effort today at what happened yesterday, thinking that perhaps he could somehow make up for the loss of four friends.

The winds were strong and blew against them— stronger than they had expected. Even though the weather was clear, the planes were blown off course into

German sea lanes. An enemy ship was now filling the skies with antiaircraft fire. One pilot said later, "It was so thick . . . it looked like a blanket."

In screaming dives, the planes of the 332nd opened up with all guns on the shell-spitting Nazi destroyer. Before long they had the ship ablaze with fire and smoke. Then another direct hit and the enemy ship blew up.

The news of this victory at sea went everywhere. While it was cheered wherever it was heard, the men of the 332nd Fighter Group took their fame with quiet pleasure. These men were no longer eager young boys. Yes, they had now come back from the blow of defeat and had scored a major victory!—but they were not wild with joy. For now every man in the group was remembering four friends flying with them just one day before.

It was clear by July 1944 that Nazi Germany was losing the war. Total defeat was closer every day. The Nazis were fighting harder than ever to keep back the advance of the Allied armies, but theirs was a losing battle. American leaders had planned well.

Just when the war was going well, the 332nd found it had a new kind of trouble. This time it was not trouble from the enemy; it came from within. By now the attacks on Germany's oil fields were in full force. The 332nd was moved to Rametti, Italy, where they were joined by the famous 99th Fighter Squadron—the first black air squadron in the history of the U.S. Army. The 99th was to become part of the 332nd, making the all-black fighter force bigger and stronger.

Rametti (rə·mĕt′ē)

But the change was not that easy to make, for the pilots of the 99th had fought long and well in the war and did not want to belong to a group of flyers they thought were still young and untried.

The men of the 332nd had their own problems with the change. True, they had not fought as much as the 99th, but they felt they were just as able. Slowly but surely, the new and bigger 332nd split into two unfriendly camps.

Colonel Davis saw what was happening. He knew that unless his men worked together they could not fight well. This kind of problem could be more dangerous for the 332nd Fighter Group than the enemy. He understood that working out the problem would be up to him.

He convinced the men that the only reason they were there was to fight and win the war. They were trained fighter pilots and their one job was to destroy the enemy, not one another.

The men of the 332nd got the message and they took comfort. Their number had grown, the group had gained experience, and now they could all see that they had to work together to win.

All this time the enemy was hard at work—fixing what weapons they could still use to fight, setting up new lines of supply, and building new supply stations in different places. These stations now had to be destroyed by the Allies. The American bombers went out on raids seventeen days a month. The new 332nd went along on many of these missions, fighting off groups of enemy planes sent to destroy the B-24 bombers over Rumania, Austria, and Bohemia.

The men of the 332nd came back from each mission with a new story and a new hero. One such hero was Capt. Joseph D. Elsberry, a young officer who always seemed ready to go into battle. Three Nazi pilots found this out about him the morning of July 12. Captain Elsberry was leading a fighter group that day whose job was protecting American bombers. Elsberry spotted enemy planes coming in and radioed his men to prepare their ships for a fight, which meant dropping their extra fuel. The planes could move better in a fight if they were lighter.

By this time the P-47s had dropped back. The bombers went on alone to finish their mission. The Nazis, seeing the gas tanks falling from the fighter planes and thinking the small planes were dropping bombs, turned away from the bombers and started after the fighters instead.

The Nazi pilots made their move a moment too late, though. By the time they turned away from the bombers, the 332nd fighter pilots, led by Captain Elsberry, were already on their tails.

The captain lined up his gun sight and fired a short burst. Although the side of one Nazi plane blew away, Elsberry kept on its tail. He fired again; the enemy plane went out of control, slipped off to the right, and fell to the earth.

A moment later a second enemy plane flashed by. Elsberry rolled his plane in a steep turn and started firing. The Nazi plane began to smoke, fell into a dive, and plunged to the ground.

As he pulled out of his turn, Elsberry caught sight of another enemy plane. As it quickly shot across his path in a sharp dive, Elsberry rolled to his left and went after the plane. Then he started firing. The Nazi twisted and turned the plane to avoid Elsberry. He was a good pilot, but not as good as the American.

The Nazi pilot continued his dive. Down he went, hoping to avoid the American on his tail. Just before reaching the ground he tried to pull out of his dive. It was too late. The plane crashed into the ground, leaving a ball of fire to mark the spot where it hit the green land below.

By the end of the month almost all the enemy's oil fields had been bombed by the Allies. Soon there was not even half the oil the Nazi army needed for fuel. This was the beginning of the end for Hitler's Germany. And hints of the next big step were in the air. The Allies would invade Germany itself.

"Destroy everything that moves!" was the order. "We are moving into Germany."

The job for the 332nd was to finish their work as well as they had started it. Their days together from the time they were eager young cadets had brought them down a long, hard path. Many had been lost on the way, but those who were left knew that they would now set the stage for the biggest part in the war. An invasion by Allied ground troops was around the corner. And then—*the end of the war!*

The day came when the 332nd was given time out from fighting. There was something going on—something special. Everyone could feel it and the men shared the feeling with winks and grins. Then the official word came from army chiefs in Washington, D.C. On September 10, four pilots of the fighter group were to get awards for all they had done in service to their country.

The day was to be special in another way. Col. Benjamin O. Davis, Jr., was also to be honored. And Gen. Benjamin O. Davis, Sr., his father, was flying in to present the awards. The general was the highest ranking black officer in the U.S. Army.

The men of the 332nd were all "spit-and-polish" as the ceremony began. All eyes were on General Davis. Smartly marching up to the stand, he spoke to his son.

"I am very proud of you," he said.

Everyone there felt something special pass between father and son. Both had a look in their eyes that everyone understood. Then the general went on to read the army's message to the men of the 332nd.

> For extraordinary achievement in an aerial flight as pilot of a P-47 type aircraft. Faced with the problem of protecting the larger bomber formation with the comparatively few fighters under his control, Colonel Davis so skillfully disposed his squadron that the bomber formation suffered few losses.

aerial—*in the air*
disposed—*arranged or set up*

The following four men of the 332nd also got awards that day:

Capt. Alfonso Davis: *He led an attack on an enemy airfield at Grozwardin, Rumania, on August 30. The 332nd destroyed 83 planes on the ground in this raid.*

Capt. Joseph D. Elsberry: *Battled his way to his targets, defeating the enemy in the air and destroying his vital installation on the ground.*

First Lt. Clarence D. Lester: *With complete disregard for his personal safety he destroyed three enemy fighters, thus preventing the enemy from making concentrated attacks on the bombers.*

Lt. Jack D. Holsclaw: *With complete disregard for his personal safety . . . with an outstanding display of daring and combat skill, destroyed two enemy fighters and forced the remainder to break off their organized attacks.*

Every man of the 332nd took satisfaction in these awards. They understood that the honors given to their friends were very much their own. Each man knew he had done his share.

And the men of the 332nd continued to do their share throughout the rest of the war in Europe. Finally, at midnight on May 8, 1945, the fighting in Europe was over. The Allies had beaten the Nazis. The bloodshed and killing on European battlefields and in the air had ended.

And then, once again, on June 8, 1945, Col. Benjamin Davis was honored. This time he was given the Silver Star for bravery in combat. The commanding general of the 15th Air Force said of Colonel Davis: *He is a fine soldier and has done wonders with the 332nd. I am positive that no other man in our air corps could have handled this job in the manner he has.*

Grozwardin (grōz·vär′dĭn)

The 332nd had been overseas for 22 months. During that time 450 black pilots had joined its ranks. They flew nearly 1,600 missions and over 15,000 air flights. They had proven that color was not important among fighting soldiers. No one race of people owned the will or courage to fight bravely and win. Nor did any one race of people own a love for their country.

On October 17, 1945, the fighter group was awarded the Presidential Distinguished Unit Citation, the highest award that can be given to an army unit.

Their skill and daring made all the Red Tails outstanding as pilots and as Americans. They cut a path of honor for those who would follow in America's fighting forces.

Character Theme—Courage & Sacrifice

God's Word Says
Proverbs 3:27

Withhold not good from them to whom it is due, when it is in the power of thine hand to do it.

Time to Think

1. In what war did the Red Tails fight?
2. What is noteworthy about the Fighting Red Tails?
3. What was special about Col. Benjamin Davis's award on September 10?
4. How many missions did the 332nd fly in the 22 months it was overseas?

Credits